# the Forth Naturalist and Historian

## Volume 24

Published by the Forth Naturalist and Historian, University of Stirling – an approved charity and member of the Scottish Publishers Association. 2001.

ISSN 0309-7560

ISBN 1-898008-42-6

Supported by BP in Scotland.

Cover: front– Loch Katrine by Lavery, courtesy of the National Gallery of Scotland.
    back– Spiders – *Pardosa nigriceps* and *Tetragnatha extensa*, courtesy of Dick Jones.

Printed by Meigle Printers Ltd., Tweedbank Industrial Estate, Galashiels.
Set in Zapf Calligraphic on Edixion 100 gsm and cover Go Gloss Art 250 gsm.

# POLLEN ANALYSES AND HISTORIC LANDSCAPE CHANGE AT ASHENTROOL, MENSTRIE GLEN

Richard Tipping, Richard Waldron and David C. Cowley

## Introduction

Menstrie Glen, a small valley at the western end of the Ochils, preserves an extensive relict farming landscape of medieval and later date. Combined archaeological survey by the Royal Commission on the Ancient and Historical Monuments of Scotland and documentary searches by John Harrison (RCAHMS forthcoming) have illuminated the history of farming and settlement of the glen over the last *circa* 500 years. This brief report summarises the history of the vegetation and land use change as seen by a set of detailed, though tentatively dated, pollen analyses of a small peat deposit at Ashentrool, in the northern part of the survey area (Figure 1). The analyses provide insights into the landscape history of this part of Menstrie Glen over about the last 300 years, which complement those drawn from the archaeological and documentary survey.

## The Site, Methods of Analysis and Presentation of Results

Ashentrool (NGR NN 827 004) is in the upper reaches of Menstrie Glen. The site sampled is a small peat deposit, some 200 m in diameter and 1.78 m deep at the point sampled, lying on a broad terrace at 315 m OD on the western flank of Loss Hill (Figure 1). The peat deposit formed initially in a small pond, though when is not known, dammed behind a rock-bar that is being cut through by a small west-flowing stream. Immediately adjacent to the peat deposit relict cultivation remains are visible, occupying areas of well-drained brown forest soils of the Balrownie Association, and later 'herring-bone' drainage ditches can be seen on the shallow hill and valley-floor peat.

The topmost 60 cm of peat were sampled with a 100 cm closed-chamber Russian corer, transported in clean plastic guttering to the laboratory, and stored at 4°C. Twenty-two sub-samples were prepared for analysis by standard chemical techniques (Moore *et al.*, 1991). Stained residues from this treatment were counted to sums of at least 300 land pollen grains (Figure 2) on an Olympus CH2 binocular microscope at magnification x400, and x1000 for critical determinations and size measurements. Only selected taxa recorded at more than two horizons are presented in Figure 2; full counts are available in Waldron (1997). Pollen taxa were identified from standard keys and reference collections. Pollen types in Figure 2 are those of Moore *et al.* (1991). Data are drawn as percentages of total land pollen (tlp), *i.e.*, for pollen types thought to derive from dryland surfaces, or tlp+group for pollen types and spores not seen as of terrestrial origin.

Dating of events is currently based on the occurrence of spruce (*Picea*) pollen in contiguous peat samples above a depth of 6 cm below the surface. It is assumed that this pollen originates from one or all of three coniferous plantations within 2 km of the site. The largest of these was planted between 1948 and 1954, and, allowing 15 years for abundant pollen production, the appearance of spruce at 6 cm is assigned a tentative age of AD 1965. Ages prior to this in the core are extrapolated on a linear peat accumulation rate of 5 yr cm$^{-1}$ or 0.2 cm yr$^{-1}$. The basal sample at 52 cm is given an age of AD 1725. Dates quoted in the following sections are rounded to the decade and should be treated as indicative rather than absolute.

### Interpretation and Discussion

From the earliest times depicted in the pollen diagram, the landscape around Ashentrool was being exploited for agriculture. Between about 1725 (52 cm) and 1800 (36 cm) there are very high percentages of cereal pollen and, although light microscopy cannot distinguish between oats (*Avena*) and wheat (*Triticum*), it is very likely that in this upland setting the pollen record represents oats. Cereal pollen grains do not disperse far, and the values recorded here in excess of 15 % total land pollen represent a substantial area given over to crops, almost certainly from the cultivated ground adjacent to the peat deposit (Figure 1). Associated weed taxa from the fields may include species of fat hen (*Chenopodiaceae*) and the daisy family (*Compositae*). It is interesting that this area of well-drained soils, at over 300 m OD, was being cultivated throughout the 18th century, and comparable patterns have been identified in Southern Scotland (Tipping, 1998). This arable capability of the uplands of Scotland supports the view that the widespread change from arable to pastoral landuse that occurred during the 18th and 19th centuries was driven by economic, social and technological changes, rather than caused by repeated crop failure through climate-induced stresses during the 'little ice age' (Parry, 1978).

Grazing was also a significant landuse in the 18th century. Proportions of wild grass pollen (*Gramineae* <8μm anl-D; Figure 2) are high, as are those of grassland herbs associated with grazing, such as ribwort plantain (*Plantago lanceolata*) and species of tormentil (*Potentilla*), bedstraws (*Galium*), buttercups (*Ranunculus*) and docks (*Rumex*). Ling (*Calluna*) heath had not been a significant component of the vegetation around the pollen site in the last 300 years, and any form of woodland was equally uncommon. It is likely that only limited numbers of scrubby alder (*Alnus* cf. *A. glutinosa*), birch (*Betula*) and hazel (*Corylus/Myrica*) trees existed near the peat bog. No original or primary woodland survived into the later historic period.

After about 1800 (36 cm) it is likely that cultivation of oats ceased in the locality, although there are sporadic occurrences of single grains of *Avena/Triticum* and associated weed taxa above 40 cm. Pasture replaced the ploughland, but the transition to a pasture-dominated landscape was neither direct nor straightforward. For a short period, possibly around 90 years from 1800 (36-20 cm), the proportions of alder and birch pollen increased. This may represent an increasing population of trees, but this is not certain given the lifespan of these trees and the short period represented. Surviving trees may have simply increased pollen production. The trees themselves probably colonised damp areas, perhaps on the peat of the valley floor itself. Willow (*Salix*) is often associated with wetlands, and the pollen becomes increasingly common after 1800, despite willow being a very low pollen producer.

The reduction of percentages of wild grasses in this phase need not represent a significant loss of pasture to woodland. These wetland trees may have formed a screen between the dry slopes that formerly supported cereal crops and the sampling site, so that their proximity to the pollen site over-represents their spatial importance. However, for a time grazing may not have been sufficiently intense to suppress the trees from flowering, or possibly seedling regeneration. The woodland may have been fenced, preventing animals from browsing on the trees. Alternatively the valley floor may have become wetter and perhaps too treacherous for animals. Sedges (*Cyperaceae*) increased after about 1850 (28 cm) and this may have been a response to the 19th century drainage ditches in the wetter hill peat (John Harrison, pers. comm.).

The woodland was removed, possibly quite abruptly at around 1900 (20 cm). The expansion of grass pollen (*Gramineae* <8μm anl-D) during the 20th century probably represents grazed pasture. This pasture maintains much of its earlier, but admittedly limited species diversity, and all associated grassland herb taxa recorded in the 18th century are also present in the near-surface samples. The maintenance of some species diversity here contrasts with intensive sheep-grazing lands in the Scottish Borders, where the present grasslands have been heavily over-grazed in the last 250 years (Tipping, 2000).

## Summary

The pollen sequence at Ashentrool is poorly dated, but appears to indicate two contrasting types of agricultural activity over the last 300 years. Cereal cultivation, probably of oats, was a major component of the landuse prior to about 1800. Replacement of cultivated fields by pasture appears to have been sudden, with former fields being turned over to grazing. The brief establishment of scrubby fen woodland at this change in landuse is difficult to interpret, but need not represent any dereliction or abandonment of the land at this site, perhaps representing no more than a discrete stand of trees on an area of wet ground. In broad terms this confirms the pattern of major landuse change in the second half of the 18th century revealed by the archaeological and historical work in Menstrie Glen, as landowners removed their tenants and established the large sheep farms that dominate the Ochils today.

## Acknowledgements

Drs Jane Bunting, Althea Davies and Paula Milburn provided assistance in pollen identification. John Harrison kindly discussed many of the issues raised in this paper and Strat Halliday commented on the text. Figure 1 is the work of

Rob Shaw and is Crown Copyright – RCAHMS. George Mitchell kindly provided access to the site.

This paper has been published with the aid of a grant from the Royal Commission on the Ancient and Historical Monuments of Scotland.

## References

Moore, P.D., Webb, J.A. and Collinson, M.E. 1991. *Pollen Analysis*. Oxford: Blackwell.

Parry, M.L. (1978). *Climate Change, Agriculture and Settlement*. Folkestone: Dawson.

RCAHMS. forthcoming. *Menstrie Glen – a Medieval and later Farming Landscape*. Edinburgh.

Tipping, R. (1998). Cereal cultivation on the Anglo-Scottish border during the 'Little Ice Age'. In *On The Edge – Human Settlement In Marginal Areas* (ed. C. Mills and G. Coles) pp1-11, Oxford: BAR.

Tipping, R. (2000). Palaeoecological approaches to historical problems: a comparison of sheep-grazing intensities in the Cheviot Hills in the Medieval and later periods. In *Townships to Farmsteads. Rural Settlement Studies in Scotland, England and Wales* (ed. J.A. Aitkinson, I. Banks and G. MacGregor) pp130-134, Oxford: BAR.

Waldron, R. B. (1997). *Historic Landscape Change on Sheriffmuir – A Palynological Approach*. Unpublished B.Sc. Dissertation, University of Stirling.

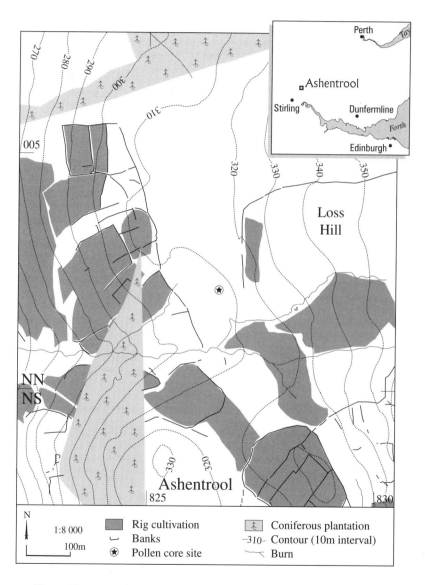

Figure 1  Location of sample site and plan of adjacent archaeological features.

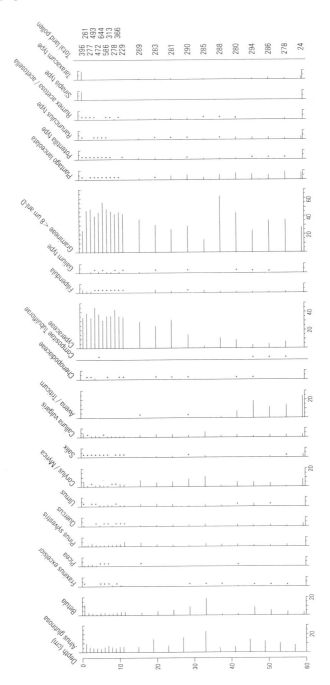

Figure 2  Pollen diagram of selected taxa at Ashentrool.

# THE WEATHER OF 2000

## S.J. Harrison

### Introduction

2000 was yet another warm year, with the monthly mean maximum air temperature at the University Climate Station (Parkhead) being above average for eleven of the twelve months. The first three months were particularly warm, especially March which was 2°C warmer than average. With the warmth came plenty of rain, which was well above average in January and February. April was a cold and wet interlude, with some late snow, before the summer made an early start in May. Although the months May to July were drier than average, the overall picture was one of changeability, although there were some lengthy spells of very warm weather. August was very warm at times but thunderstorms, which are relatively rare in the Forth valley, made this a wet month. The remaining months, from September onwards, were generally warm and very wet until snow arrived late in December.

*(The rainfall and temperature values in the following refer to the University (Parkhead) or Bridge of Allan climate stations)*

**January** Mild. Sunny at times

Over the first eleven days the predominantly westerly wind reached gale force at times and rain fell on every day. The wind was exceptionally strong in the far north of Scotland on the 3rd. The 4th, 5th and 7th were blustery days, with heavy rain and sleet falling in a stormy south-westerly wind. By the 13th the skies had cleared, heralding a spell of dry weather which lasted until the 27th. However, the absence of a cloud cover resulted in moderate night frosts. Visibility was excellent in the cold Polar air. By the 27th a westerly wind had reasserted its influence on the weather and the remaining days of the month were generally wet and, at times, very windy. The 48 hr rainfall total for the 30th and 31st was 34.4 mm.

**February** Very mild but with frequent rain

The month started on a wet note with the Allan in flood following the late January rain. The unsettled weather, with occasionally strong winds and heavy rain, continued for almost the whole of the month and a daily rainfall of 1.0 mm or more was registered on 22 occasions. The wind remained strong south-westerly, almost without break, from the afternoon of the 6th through to the 11th. Sleet fell on the 8th, and by the 11th heavy snow was falling, which continued to fall throughout the 12th. The snow melted very quickly on the 14th in steady drizzle. Over the following four days there were occasional bright spells but snow or sleet fell again on the 15th and 17th. There were two bright and sunny days after the 19th, but more rain arrived from the west on the 20th. Mild air arrived on the 21st and by the 23rd the daytime temperature had reached 11.3°C (10.9°C Bridge of Allan). The very changeable pattern persisted until the end of the month, with further snow on the 24th and 28th. Over the three days 26-28th, 32.1 mm of rain was registered. The 28th was an exceptionally stormy day with hail, sleet and snow accompanied by thunder and lightning.

**March**  Warm and dry

The weather remained changeable for the first three days and further snow fell on the 3rd. The 4th was bright after a moderate frost, but the following eight days were very mild in a fresh to strong south-westerly or westerly wind. Rain was recorded on most days but there were also some lengthy spells of bright and clear weather. The temperature reached 14.6°C on the 8th, and the daffodils in Bridge of Allan had been coaxed into bloom by the 12th. The wind went round to a colder direction and hail showers fell on the 14th, but the weather remained bright and sunny until the 21st when cloud returned. Rain fell on the 23rd and 24th which was heavy at times, but the following days were calm and dry with increasing amounts of bright sunshine. Low cloud returned on the 29th and the last three days of the month were mostly dull and damp with a few sunny spells.

**April**  Cold and wet

The month started in a cold north-easterly airflow. The maximum of 10.9°C on the 1st contrasted with only 4.6°C on the 2nd. Snow began to fall, which arrived in Scotland late on the 1st. Snow and sleet showers fell throughout the day on the 2nd and 3rd. The snow eventually cleared, and the 5th to the 8th were bright sunny spring days, although night temperatures fell sharply. The grass minimum temperature fell to –7.2°C in Bridge of Allan in the early hours of the 5th. Clouds returned on the 9th bringing an end to the frosts. The weather was unsettled between the 14th and 18th and hail fell in isolated showers. From the 19th the weather became warm with some longer spells of rain, and thunder was heard on the 24th. The 26th was an exceptionally wet and windy day. There was a remarkable east-west gradient of rainfall, with heavy falls and floods in Edinburgh but only 6.2 mm on Flanders Moss. Warm Tropical air arrived from the south on the 27th resulting in a sharp rise in temperature, which reached 20.9°C (21.7°C Bridge of Allan) on the 30th.

**May**  Warm and dry at the beginning, but becoming cool and unsettled

The first fourteen days were dry and occasionally very warm but there were intermittent dull spells of weather with low cloud in the early morning, which had usually been cleared by the sun before mid-day. The warmest days were the 9th and 14th, the latter reaching 23.4°C (25.8°C Bridge of Allan). A sharp change in the weather arrived on the 15th as rain began to fall in a freshening south-westerly wind. The drop in daytime temperature was dramatic, struggling to only 13.4°C on the 17th, 10°C cooler than three days earlier.

Unsettled weather continued for much of the remainder of the month but rainfall amounts were relatively small, and there were some lengthy sunny spells. The daytime temperatures, however, hovered around a cool 15°C.

**June**  Rather changeable but becoming warm and dry mid-month

The unsettled weather pattern continued for much of the first two weeks with a conveyor-belt of cloud coming in from the west, but amounts of rain were mostly rather small. Although there were long sunny spells, some days were very dull and cold. The temperature had risen sharply by the morning of the 12th, reaching 20.4°C by the early afternoon despite a strong south-westerly wind and occasional rain. While much of northern Scotland remained cloudy and wet, the southern half shared with the rest of the British Isles in a spell of very warm weather between the 17th and 19th, the temperature reaching 27.3°C (28.8°C Bridge of Allan) on the 18th. Heavy rain fell on the morning of the 21st (10.8 mm Bridge of Allan) but the weather was cloudy, cooler and generally quite dry, from the 24th.

**July**  Rather changeable again, but very dry

The first five days were warm and cloudy, but cooler Polar air arrived on 6th. The daytime temperatures were well below average, reaching only 15.2°C on the 9th, which was also an exceptionally wet day. There was torrential rain during the early afternoon of the 9th and the local rainfall totals were 28.9 mm (Parkhead) and 33.3 mm (Bridge of Allan). By St Swithin's Day (15th) the weather had become sunny, dry and warm. Accordingly, the following nine days were glorious high summer with the daytime temperature exceeding 20.0°C on almost every day. Although the temperature remained high, conditions became very muggy and at times unpleasantly humid from the 25th. Thunder was heard on the 28th and 29th and an otherwise mostly dry month finished with a very wet finale.

**August**  Unsettled and rather wet

The 1st and 2nd were dull with rain but occasional sunny spells gradually began to develop. The cloud cover had cleared on the 6th in time for the Strathallan Games, which took place on a warm sunny day with a light westerly breeze. The settled weather began to break on the 8th and the 9th was a dull and very wet day with low cloud obscuring the hills after the warmest night of the year at 15.7°C. The weather remained unsettled with a mixture of rain and sun. Thunderstorms began late on the 18th, which continued intermittently until the 21st. These were associated with some exceptionally heavy precipitation which fell as hail on the 19th and 21st. The hailstones on the 19th were reported to be as large as 15 mm in diameter. The weather became more settled from the 21st and there was morning fog on the 23rd and 25th. The fog cleared quickly and days were sunny and very warm, reaching 24.5°C on the 25th. More rain arrived from the west late on the 25th, and the 26th was a dull and very wet day with a heavy thunderstorm in the evening.

The weather continued changeable and a little cool for the remainder of the month with a mixture of rain and lengthy sunny spells.

**September**  Warm and very wet

After a dull start, the weather freshened on the 2nd as a light northerly breeze set in. There were two calm and sunny days on the 3rd and 4th, although night temperatures fell to 5.2°C. Rain came in from the west late on the 4th and the weather became rather changeable in a fresh south-westerly wind. By the 9th the weather had become very dull, and heavy continuous rain fell on the 11th, resulting in flooding on the Allan. The 48 h rainfall on the 10th/11th amounted to 39.8 mm in Bridge of Allan. There was further rain on the 17th and 18th and the weather remained very unsettled until the end of the month, with lengthy spells of heavy continuous rain, most notably on the 21st, 26th and 27th.

**October**  Mild and rather wet

Unsettled weather prevailed for most of the month, which proved to be the wettest October in England and Wales since 1903. The first of many stormy spells arrived late on the 3rd (8.5 mm) which was also the last really warm day of the year (maximum 20.7°C). A bright day followed on the 5th in the wake of the storm, before more rain arrived on the 6th. Exceptionally heavy rain fell on the 9th (30.0 mm. 33.7 mm Bridge of Allan) and by the end of the day the Allan was in flood. There was a bright interlude on the 13th and the weather remained quite dry in a light south-westerly breeze on the 14th and 15th. This pattern of rain and wind followed by sunshine and showers arrived with almost mathematical regularity until the end of the month. On the 28th more heavy rain fell during the evening and overnight (28.7 mm Bridge of Allan) and by the 29th the Allan was in flood again.

**November**  Very variable. At times very cold and generally cloudy and wet

There was a spell of bright weather over the first four days during which the visibility was excellent. However, under clear skies night temperatures began to fall and the first air frost of the winter was recorded in Bridge of Allan on the morning of the 2nd, and at Parkhead by the 5th. The 6th was a very wet day in a strong north-easterly wind and registered a rainfall of 39.0 mm, the wettest day of the year (38.7 mm Bridge of Allan). There was further rain between the 10th and 13th. As the cloud cover cleared on the 13th, the air temperature fell below freezing and there were two crisp winter days before rain returned on the 15th. Although the weather chart had an unsettled look to it, conditions remained relatively dry between the 16th and 20th. Wet weather arrived from the south-west on the 21st and the remainder of the month was generally rather dull and damp with only occasional glimpses of the sun. The persistent cloud cover did, however, keep night frosts away.

**December** Wet again; becoming much colder

The weather patterns remained unchanged from November but the air was mild. The rainfall total for the first five days came to 29.1 mm (40.8 mm Bridge of Allan) and the water table was at the surface across the carse lands. After a brief dry interlude on the 6th, rain and strong winds returned on the 7th and a further 35.2 mm (44.7 mm Bridge of Allan) fell over six days. A cold northerly wind developed late on the 13th and by the morning of the 15th the air temperature had fallen to –2.2°C (–4.1°C Bridge of Allan) in the cold Arctic air. The daytime temperature reached only 1.4°C and 1.3°C in Bridge of Allan on the 16th and 17th. There was heavy rain on the 19th (18.8 mm) after which there three very dull and damp days on the 20th, 21st and 22nd. From the 23rd the air temperature fell sharply in a cold easterly airflow and there were light snow showers on Christmas Day. Dense freezing fog formed during the 26th and the daytime temperature failed to rise above –0.5°C. The fog persisted all day on the 27th and the temperature in Bridge of Allan reached only –4.0°C by mid-day. Heavy snow began to fall during the evening of the 27th and by the morning of the 28th this had caused widespread disruption across the UK. The clouds cleared away by the 29th and the night minimum temperature fell to –8.7°C in Bridge of Allan (ground minimum –11.1°C), freezing the remaining snow cover. Calm weather continued into the 30th but heavy snow began to fall during the afternoon of the 31st

**Noteworthy weather events in Scotland during 2000**

In terms of exceptional weather, Scotland escaped relatively lightly during 2000, with most of the drama happening south of the border in England and Wales

- January 3rd: severe gales hit Northern and Western Scotland. Thousands of homes were without power in Northern Scotland and all ferries to the Northern Isles were cancelled. Winds were exceptionally strong in the Western Isles and there were blizzards on Cairngorm.
- January 29/30th: gales with gusts exceeding 90 kts affected Northern Scotland again.
- April 26th: exceptionally heavy rain in Eastern Scotland resulted in flooding in parts of Edinburgh, and heavy falls also occurred around Stirling. However, only a little distance to the west, very little rain fell at Flanders Moss.
- June 12th/13th: a record-breaking low pressure (centre 966 mb) resulted in strong winds across Scotland. There were gusts in excess of 70 kts in western Scotland. Falling trees blocked roads and brought down power lines.
- Between the 18th and 21st August there were widespread thunderstorms which were accompanied by heavy rain and hail.
- September 11th: heavy rain in Scotland caused flash flooding and some road and rail closures.
- October 9th: deep depression over southern Scotland resulted in very heavy rain and some flooding.

- October 29th/30th: Heavy rain over much of Scotland which fell as snow in some areas.
- December 27th: Heavy snowfall which closed some airports. 20 cm of snow lying in Glasgow.

### Bridge of Allan Flood Diary 2000

The Allan overtopped its banks near Bridge of Allan on the following dates: 1st February, 27th February, 11th September, 9th October, 29th October.

### Scottish Snowfall Changes Project

Maps have been produced which estimate the number of days with snow lying which may be expected in the 2020s, 2050s and the 2080s. These have been based on climatic analogues. The final report on the research, which was commissioned by the Scottish Executive, was published in May 2001.

Changes in the number of days on which snow is lying on the ground during the winter months as a result of large scale change in climate has implications for both the economy and the environment of Scotland. The greatest effects will be felt in the winter tourism sector where opportunities for skiing and ice climbing are likely to be greatly reduced. There are further knock-on effects for related activities such as accommodation, catering, retailing and local employment. However, with some adaptation it is likely that Scotland can continue to offer opportunities to engage in these activities. The clearing of snow from the roads should become less of a problem, but the variable nature of the Scottish climate will always make it necessary to remain prepared for the occasionally heavy snowfall. Greater access to the land during the winter will mean that operations such as logging could continue but there will be a temptation for greater numbers of walkers to get into the hills. This may cause more trampling damage and could also disturb wildlife. Floods may become more frequent during the winter months but less frequent in spring, which will affect water-resource management, hydro-electric power generation and river habitats.

### Reference

Harrison S.J., Winterbottom S.J. and Johnson R.C. (2001) *Climate Change and Changing Snowfall Patterns in Scotland* Scottish Executive Environment Group Research Findings No.14. Edinburgh. The Stationery Office.

*This report is based on the Annual Climatological Bulletin of the University of Stirling, copies of which may be obtained from the author, S.J. Harrison, at the Department of Environmental Science, University of Stirling, Stirling FK9 4LA*

# THIRTY YEARS OF WEATHER OBSERVATION AT PARKHEAD

## S.J. Harrison

## Introduction

Weather observation on the campus of the University of Stirling began in 1969 and has since provided a vital supply of information for a variety of research projects in the natural sciences. The observations were first published in the Monthly Weather Report of the Meteorological Office in January 1971 and so, by the end of 2000, the continuous record had reached the benchmark of thirty years, which is the standard averaging period for climatological normals. To mark the occasion, the following report places on record a short history of observation at the station and describes some of the principal features of the local climate that the records have revealed.

## History

When the University of Stirling was founded in 1967 there were almost no suitable climate stations capable of providing a reliable flow of climatic information to support ongoing research in the biological sciences. The nearest station, at Stirling (Batterflats) (NS 786 925), had been established at the beginning of the 20th Century but the site had been encroached upon by urban development around Stirling, and observation eventually ceased during 1982. Falkirk and Grangemouth stations were distant from the University and experienced a much stronger climatic influence from the Forth Estuary than would be the case in Stirling. The other station, which also closed in the early 1980's, was at Earl's Hill (NS 725 882), to the south-west of Stirling, but this was at an elevation of 335 m (1100 ft). Support for the establishment of a new climate station was received from the Meteorological Office in 1969 and the site was officially named "Parkhead" in a letter dated 21st May 1969 to Dr S. Matthews of Biological Sciences. The name, which has not proved to be either helpful or appropriate, came from Parkhead Farm which, although less than 1km away from the station, is 100 m higher above sea-level. In retrospect 'Airthrey' or 'Logie' would have been more appropriate. As it is, the station has shared its name with a famous football ground, which has at least provided some amusement for the many school groups who have visited over the years.

The first official return of observations to the Meteorological Office, on METFORM 3208A, was made in 1970. The Office commented on the exceptionally high standard of the return. Publication of the observations from Parkhead in the Monthly Weather Report of the Meteorological Office began from January 1971, the year temperatures changed from Fahrenheit to Celsius.

In 1993 the University of Stirling produced draft plans for new residences in the immediate proximity of the Parkhead station, as a result of which it was moved to a new location a little over 100 m away (Figure 1). In 1994 the

University agreed that the new station should be located in the Memorial Garden between the existing site and Alexander Court, a group of student residences. Equipment for the new station was purchased by the University, which also provided the enclosure. The new station would continue the name and be referred to as Parkhead II. The new station became fully operational from January 1995. As there were slight differences in siting characteristics, particularly with regard to shelter, both old and new stations were operated between January and September 1995 in order to ensure homogeneity in the climatic record.

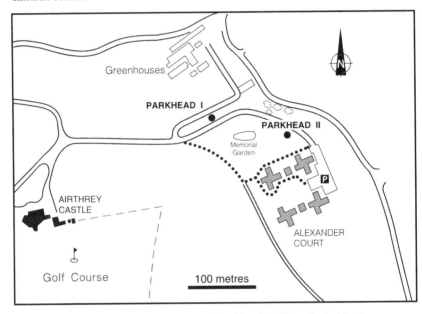

Figure 1. Location of Parkhead I and Parkhead II Climatological Stations

**Site Characteristics**

*Parkhead I (1970–1995)*

Grid reference ..................... NS 815 969
Height above sea-level ..... 35 m
Aspect ................................. South-east
Shelter index ...................... 33.2 Slightly sheltered

The station was located in the University gardens in the north-east corner of the campus. Small bushes and a tall hedge lay within 10 m of the site to east, west and south. Open beds lay to the north with a steep rise to the Ochil Hills at 400 m distance. The site was, therefore, heavily sheltered from the north. The enclosure was generally maintained to a high standard and usually passed Meteorological Office inspection with only minor remedial action required.

## Parkhead II (1995–date)

Grid reference ..................... NS 816 968
Height above sea-level ..... 35 m
Aspect ................................. South-east
Shelter index ...................... 26.5 Average shelter

The station is located in the eastern corner of the Memorial Garden between the Alexander Court student residences and the former site of Parkhead. There is relatively open ground to the west, and a low (1.5 m) hedge nearby to the east and north. There are mature trees (15-18 m high) at a distance of 50 m to the north. To the south there are University residences at a distance of less than 100 m.

## Observations and Data Quality

Table 1 Principal observations at Parkhead climatological station

| Element | Description |
| --- | --- |
| Air Temperature | At 1.2 m above ground level in a thermometer screen. Maximum and minimum over 24 h 0900-0900 GMT. Dry bulb and wet bulb temperature at 0900 GMT. Surface beneath screen is bare concrete. |
| Rainfall | Total accumulated in 24 h 0900-0900 GMT in a standard raingauge with 12.5 cm orifice set at 30 cm above a grass surface. |
| Cloud Cover | Estimated by the observer in oktas (eighths) at 0900 GMT. |
| Wind Direction | Estimated by the observer to the eight principal points of compass at 0900 GMT. No wind vane. |
| Wind Speed | Estimated by the observer using the Beaufort wind scale at 0900 GMT. Wind not metered. Converted to knots using mid-points on the scale. |
| Present Weather | Estimated by the observer at 0900 GMT using international reporting codes. Not included in 3208A report. |
| Visibility | Estimated by the observer at 0900 GMT using standard reporting codes. |
| Soil Temperature | Temperature at 30 cm depth at 0900 GMT using a mercury-in-glass thermometer suspended down a metal tube. |
| State of Ground | Reported by the observer using standard reporting codes. No bare soil plot at the station. |
| Snow | Whether snow lying (50 % or more of surface within the immediate vicinity of the station) plus depth of lying snow. |

The climatic observations generated by Parkhead are specified in Table 1. Observations were made initially by Mr A Liddell of Biological Sciences at the University, but during the 1970s this responsibility was transferred to the University ground staff. Mr Liddell was responsible for completing the 3208A METFORM at the end of each month, a duty which he transferred to Mr L. Taylor on his retirement in 2000. Research staff in Biological Sciences acted as superintendent of the station until the establishment of the Department of Earth and Environmental Science in 1978 when responsibility passed to Dr S.J. Harrison.

Quality control of the observations was primarily left to the Meteorological Office until 1996 when a system of internal pre-checking was introduced. A photocopy is taken of the observers' register, which is then cross-checked against observations from Bridge of Allan, less than 2 km to the west of the station. Hard copies of monthly returns made prior to 1996 have been quality controlled retrospectively. On the whole, the quality of observing has been high. The most persistent problems have been occasional failure to re-set the maximum and/or minimum thermometers, failure to report broken thermometers, persistent use of 'TR' (trace) to register both negligible and zero daily rainfalls, and a failure to melt accumulated snow into the raingauge. Despite being next to a relatively busy thoroughfare the level of vandalism has been exceptionally low.

The daily data for the 30-year record have been quality controlled and are now available in monthly summary form as Minitab data files (Table 2) which are available as e-mail attachments or hard-copy from the author.

Table 2 Minitab data file specifications

| Minitab File Label | Variable |
|---|---|
| maximum | means of daily maximum temperatures |
| minimum | means of daily minimum temperatures |
| frosts | number of air frosts in the month |
| rainfall | total rainfall for each month |
| rainmax | highest daily rainfall in each month |
| rain02 | number of days with rainfall $\geq 0.2$ mm |
| rain10 | number of days with rainfall $\geq 1.0$ mm |
| rain50 | number of days with rainfall $\geq 5.0$ mm |

*** Monthly means, or absolute maxima (greatest falls) are included under the year code '999' and should be deleted before any analysis is undertaken of monthly data.

Monthly summaries of the observations from Parkhead were published in the Monthly Weather Report until publication of the report ceased in 1993. The data are now available via the Internet on the British Atmospheric Data Centre (BADC) web site (*www.badc.rl.ac.uk*). The University of Stirling's Annual Climatological Bulletin is based on observations from Parkhead and subsequently appears in summary form in the *Forth Naturalist and Historian*.

## Analysis of Weather Data

*Air Temperature*

Due to thermal lag in the ground surface and in the lower atmosphere, the mean maximum temperatures tend to follow the solstices, the warmest month being July (19.8°C) and the coolest January (6.5°C). The daytime temperature in summer frequently exceeds 20.0°C while in December and January there are occasional days on which the air temperature does not rise above 0.0°C. Most of the hottest days have occurred during July, with some in August, and the highest air temperature ever reached at Parkhead was 29.8°C on July 12th 1983.

The mean minimum temperatures tend to follow a similar pattern to the maxima between July (10.6°C) and January (0.5°C). The winter air temperature frequently falls below freezing with the coldest days tending to occur in either December or January. The monthly mean minimum air temperature has been below 0.0°C in six times in December and ten times in January. The lowest air temperature ever reached at Parkhead was –17.2°C on the 11th January 1982 during a protracted spell of very cold weather. In the context of local climates in the Stirling area, Parkhead is relatively well protected from air frost when compared to the low lying carse lands of the Forth valley where there are relatively more frequent frosts and a shorter frost-free season. The season of greatest frequency of frost at Parkhead is from October through to April, with the highest average frequency being in January. Late spring frosts occur in May but usually in the first half of the month, and June air frosts are extremely rare. The first of the autumn air frosts usually arrives in October but in roughly one year in four, this occurs during September.

*Rainfall*

Most of the rainfall in Stirling is associated with low atmospheric pressure with only occasional convectional storms, usually in late summer. The seasonal pattern of rainfall is typical of a mid-latitude climate in which rainfall is dominantly from depressions arriving from the Atlantic in that the wettest months are, on average, from September through to March. December and January have the highest average rainfalls. Although the summer months are relatively drier, a particular feature of the local climate is the abrupt shift from a generally wet March to a considerably drier April, this being the driest month, on average, during the year. Rainfall is extremely variable from year to year. The most variable month is March, with April being one of the most consistent.

Daily falls in excess of 25 mm are relatively frequent, particularly during the winter months. There have, however, been a number of remarkable falls during the 30 year period, most of which have resulted in local flooding (Table 3). The largest 24-hour total was recorded on November 3rd 1984, which resulted in a massive slope failure above Menstrie.

Table 3 Daily rainfalls of 40.0 mm or more. 1971-2000

| Rank | Rainfall mm | Date |
|------|-------------|------|
| 1 | 68.3 | 3rd November 1984 |
| 2 | 66.2 | 1st October 1981 |
| 3 | 65.6 | 26th July 1985 |
| 4 | 44.2 | 18th September 1985 |
| 5 | 44.0 | 25th March 1979 |
| 6 | 43.8 | 16th December 1989 |
| 7 | 40.5 | 30th November 1985 |
| 8 | 40.0 | 1st January 1991 |

The three standard thresholds of daily rainfall are 0.2 mm (rain day), 1.0 mm (wet day), and 5.0 mm (very wet day). On average 51 % of days are classified as rain-days although there is considerable year-to-year variation in this figure, ranging from 60 % in 1986 to only 43 % in 1997. Expressed in terms of percentage of days in each month, there is a well marked seasonal contrast between winter and summer months. On average 41 % can be classified as being wet, varying between winter (45-55 %) and summer (30-35 %) months. Only 18 % of days are, on average, very wet days. Only 10 % of April days are very wet, in contrast to January when the proportion is 26 %.

*Other Weather Observations*

Because of the sheltered nature of the site and the use of the Beaufort scale of wind force, a very high number of 'Calms' appears in the record. Otherwise, the most frequent wind directions are between South-West and West.

The record of soil temperature at a depth of 30 cm is discontinuous due to the change in location in 1995. At a depth of 30 cm the highest temperature has usually been reached in late July or early August and the lowest in early February.

## Climatological Normals

The quality controlled and revised climatological normals for Parkhead are as follows in Tables 4 and 5.

Table 4 Climatological Normals for Parkhead 1971-2000 (Temperature)

| Month | Maximum Temperature °C | Minimum Temperature °C | Number of Air Frosts |
|---|---|---|---|
| January | 6.5 | 0.5 | 13 |
| February | 6.9 | 0.8 | 11 |
| March | 9.1 | 1.9 | 7 |
| April | 11.8 | 3.4 | 4 |
| May | 15.3 | 5.8 | 1 |
| June | 17.7 | 8.4 | <1 |
| July | 19.8 | 10.6 | 0 |
| August | 19.4 | 10.2 | 0 |
| September | 16.3 | 8.3 | <1 |
| October | 12.9 | 5.4 | 2 |
| November | 9.2 | 2.6 | 8 |
| December | 7.2 | 1.1 | 11 |
| YEAR | 12.7 | 4.9 | 57 |

Table 5 Climatological Normals for Parkhead 1971-2000 (Rainfall)

| Month | Total Rainfall mm | Greatest Fall mm | Number of days ≥ 0.2 mm | Number of days ≥ 1.0 mm | Number of days ≥ 5.0 mm |
|---|---|---|---|---|---|
| January | 110.7 | 40.0 | 19 | 16 | 8 |
| February | 73.2 | 31.8 | 16 | 12 | 5 |
| March | 81.4 | 44.0 | 17 | 14 | 5 |
| April | 47.5 | 35.3 | 13 | 10 | 3 |
| May | 56.9 | 28.3 | 14 | 11 | 4 |
| June | 57.1 | 35.8 | 13 | 10 | 4 |
| July | 62.9 | 65.5 | 13 | 10 | 5 |
| August | 68.1 | 30.0 | 14 | 11 | 5 |
| September | 87.7 | 44.2 | 15 | 12 | 6 |
| October | 97.9 | 66.2 | 17 | 14 | 6 |
| November | 98.9 | 68.3 | 17 | 14 | 7 |
| December | 101.0 | 43.8 | 18 | 15 | 7 |
| YEAR | 943.3 | 68.3 | 186 | 149 | 65 |

## Bibliography

Data from the station have been used in a number of research publications but those specifically relating to the climate in Central Scotland include:-

Harrison S.J. (1980) Rainfall in the Stirling Area *Forth Naturalist and Historian* 5 23-34.

Harrison S.J. and Wallace R.W .(1982) Frost in the Forth valley *Journal of Meteorology (UK)* 7, 84-86.

Harrison S.J. (1987) Climatic conditions over the Estuary and Firth of Forth *Proceedings Royal Society of Edinburgh* 93B, 245-258.

Harrison S.J. and Harrison D.J. (1988) The effect of elevation on the climatically determined growing season in the Ochil Hills *Scottish Geographical Magazine* 104, 108-115.

Harrison S.J. and Harrison D.J. (1988) The effect of altitude on freeze-thaw frequency *Journal of Meteorology (UK)* 13, 341-343.

Harrison S.J. and Harrison D.J. (1991) Characterising winters: An index for use in applied meteorology *Journal of Meteorology (UK)* 6, 329-333.

Harrison S.J. (1993) Recent changes in the weather in central Scotland *Forth Naturalist and Historian* 16, 11-24.

Harrison S.J. (1993) Climate In: *Central Scotland* (Ed. L. Corbett) pp18-31 Forth Naturalist and Historian Stirling.

Harrison S.J. (1994) Air temperatures in the Ochil Hills, Scotland: Problems with paired stations *Weather 49*, 209-215.

Harrison S.J. (1994) Climate/Weather In: *The Ochil Hills* (Corbett L., Roy E.K. and Snaddon R.C). pp15-17 Forth Naturalist and Historian/Clackmannan Field Studies Society.

Harrison S.J. (1997) Central and Southern Scotland In: *British Climates: A Regional Approach*. (Ed. Mayes J. and Wheeler D.) London. Routledge. pp205-227

Harrison S.J. (1997) Changes in the Scottish Climate *Botanical Journal of Scotland* 49, 287-300.

Harrison S.J. and Bairner J. (1997) Studies in microclimatology *Teaching Geography* 22, 173-179.

Harrison S.J. (1998) Analysing climatic data and the problem of spurious correlation: a case study *SAGT Journal* 27, 8-11.

# FORTH AREA BIRD REPORT 2000

## C.J. Henty

Seventy eight contributors appear this year, some sending individual notes either direct to the Editor or via the RSPB local group, others have assisted in the wildfowl counts and the breeding birds survey. The extensive use of record cards has greatly helped the compilation of notes by species, please send in these cards arranged in the species order as in this report or in standard field guides and lists (at least roughly), please not alphabetical. Red Kites and Ospreys continue to do fairly well and are now seen more extensively in the area whilst Goldeneye again attempted nesting, but this year it was unsuccessful. Corncrakes were heard around the edge of Flanders Moss. A new species for the area is Mediterranean Gull, found on the Forth near the gull concentration at Fallin – not entirely unexpected since this species has been seen regularly in the outer Firth of Forth. Amongst winter visitors the drake Smew at L.Dochart has shown again, on the estuary the Grangemouth flock of Pintails shows remarkable consistency in location and numbers, but further downstream Great Crested Grebes continue to be only in small groups. There are some interesting reports of ringed Whooper Swans. Several Greenshanks and Green Sandpipers wintered, however the autumn passage of the scarcer waders was weak, in particular only two Little Stints were recorded. This may be connected with the scarcity of easterly winds this autumn which presumably also affected the late and generally weak influx of Scandinavian thrushes. One notable migrant was a Wryneck at Grangemouth, some Waxwings appeared in December.

This report is compiled from a larger archive of records submitted to the local recorder under the national scheme organised by the Scottish Ornithologists Club; annual Bird Reports depend entirely on contributions from the local birdwatching community, as far as possible these are acknowledged with initials as well as the full name list in the introduction. However, this year the compilation process has been more complicated than usual, my apologies if any peole have been missed out. The area covered by the report comprises the council areas of Falkirk and Clackmannan together with Stirling, excluding Loch Lomondside and other parts of the Clyde drainage basin. Please note that we do not include the Endrick water, i.e Fintry and Balfron. Records from Carron Valley Reservoir are published here but it is proposed that Clyde should cover all the forest south of the reservoir.

Most months in 2000, apart from April, were warmer than average, this was most marked from January to March though there was much rain in February and in the autumn. The first week of January had strong westerly winds and heavy rain, but then high pressure dominated, dry but frosty, until the last week gave unsettled conditions and 35 mm of rain in the last two days. February continued unsettled with three days of snow in mid-month and two later, separated by very brief spells of dry weather. The first half of March stayed unsettled, then a bright and sunny third week led to a changeable end. North-east winds in early April produced two days of snow and cold conditions, the second half was much wetter and warmer. After a warm and dry start to May the second half became unsettled and much cooler, this continued until the third week of June when it became very warm and then stayed fairly dry but cloudy. Early July was warmer but still cloudy, then a cooler spell, with torrential rain on the 9th, gave way to a sunny and warm spell. Warm but changeable conditions dominated August and September with only short sunny spells, there were thunderstorms in late August and periods of heavy rain throughout September. October continued this pattern with no settled anticyclonic spells. In November primarily cloudy and wet weather was interrupted by only two short dry and frosty periods. Cyclonic systems made the first half of December windy and wet, though mild; there followed two incursions of Arctic and continental air that brought freezing temperatures and then snow after Christmas.

The information on the breeding numbers of common species in 2000 comes primarily from the British Trust for Ornithology's Breeding Bird Survey. This is based on transect counts and is now sufficiently extensive to calculate numbers of birds recorded per ten kilometres for several habitat types, these are regularly mentioned in the species paragraphs. For less common species I can sometimes mention data in terms of the numbers of pairs or apparently occupied territories for particular locations. Several observers send in a list largely or entirely for their home locality, much of this information is not appropriate for these annual reports but it is valuable to have on record and I am keeping them in a special file. At the moment there are fifteen such lists referring to the whole district from Falkirk to Killin.

For many species the records sent in are very unrepresentative of their general distribution, this applies particularly to very common species or to those that are secretive or breed in inaccessable places. Readers can consult the the Check List published in the Forth Naturalist and Historian Vol 15, but in addition I have in this report put, after the species name, a coded summary of general distribution – which often apparently contradicts the detailed records that are published for the year.

   $B$ - Breeding status, widespread (in more than five 10 km squares)
   $b$   "   "   , local, scarce (in fewer than five 10 km squares)
   $W$ - Winter status, widespread or often in groups of more than ten.
   $w$ -   "   "   , local, scarce (local and usually fewer than ten in a group)
   $P$ - Passage (used when species is usually absent in winter, $P$ or $p$ used for widespread or local as in winter status)
   $S$ or $s$ - a few species are present in summer but do not normally breed.

   Thus $BW$ would be appropriate for Robin, $B$ for Swallow, $p$ for Ruff and $SW$ for Cormorant. No status letter is used if a species occurs less than every other year.

An asterix (*) in front of the species name means that all records received have been quoted.

The SOC has pressed for a more systematic vetting of records of species that are unusual locally, this area now has an informal panel of five – C.Henty (Recorder), A. Smith, D. Orr-Ewing, A. Blair and D. Thorogood. The judging of national UK or Scottish rarities continues as before, but we have produced for the upper Forth a list of species that are scarce locally and where the records need to be supported by either a full description or sufficient evidence to remove any reasonable doubt. This list and a background explanation have been circulated to a hard core of observers and can be got from the recorder at SOC meetings or by post. Any species which is a vagrant to the area, and most of those which are asterisked in this report, will come into this category.

The organisers for both the estuary and the inland waters parts of the national wildfowl counts (WEBS) have made available the results for this report. These often contribute to the species accounts and there is also a separate summary for inland waters which concentrates on localities.

There is an ever-increasing amount of information coming in: records on the standard species cards need only to be sorted and I would urge observers to use these wherever possible (putting several records for one species on a single card); records on sheets, whether written, hand-typed or computer-typed, need to be either retyped onto a computer database or cut and pasted onto species sheets. This is time consuming and the recorder can no longer do this systematically without extensive help from contributors; otherwise these records will be scanned on arrival and only those items seeming to be salient will be transferred to the database, all the original sheets will be kept on file but that information is very difficult to unearth and inevitably some uncopied records will in fact be important but remain hidden.

The following abbreviations have been used : AoT - apparently occupied territory, BoA - Bridge of Allan, c/n - clutch of n eggs, BBS - Breeding Bird Survey, CBC- Common Bird Census, CP - Country Park, F - Female, G – Glen, GP - gravel pit, J - juvenile, L. - Loch, NR - Nature Reserve, M - Male, ON - on nest, Res - Reservoir, SP - summer plumage, WEBS – Wetland Bird Survey, Y - young.

This report has been compiled from records submitted by:

A. Ayre, M. Anderson, M.V. Bell, A. Blair, N. Bielby, Birdline Scotland, R.A. Broad, G.J. Brock, D.M. Bryant, R. Bullman, D.J. Cameron, R. Chapman, D.&A. Christie, R.&A. Daly, R. Dawson, P. Dearing, K. Duffy, S. Easthaugh, D. Egerton, P. Glennie, J.G. Harrison, I. Henderson, C.J. Henty, D. Jones, R. Jones, D.S. Kerr, G.&E. Leisk, C.J. Mallett, L.J. Mallett, A. K McNeil, J. Nimmo, R. Nisbet, D. Orr-Ewing, G. Owens, D. Pickett, D. Rees, H. Robb, P.W. Sandeman, J. Sankie, S. Sankey, A. Smith, P. Stirling-Aird, D. Thorogood, A. Thiel, M. Trubridge, A. VanBeest, J. Wheeler, J.M. Willett, K. Wilkinson, S. Zisman.

Thanks are due to S.J. Harrison for a copy of the Annual Climatological Bulletin (2000), to J. Mitchell for a copy of the L.Lomond report, to P. Stirling-Aird for data from the Raptor Study Group, and to D.M. Bryant for the results of the estuary WEBS data.

It is with great sadness that I am unable to add the name of Bill Brackenridge to those that have assisted in compiling this report. Most readers will know that he was killed in a traffic accident in November (2000), whilst returning from the SOC annual conference. For many years he produced a wealth of field observations and helped, as Assistant Recorder, with assessing records and proof reading the draft reports, more recently he wrote a section of the species accounts. His exceptionally wide knowledge of natural history showed both in his work in conservation planning and in his consistent efforts in giving talks, leading field trips, and always being ready to help people with their queries. A full obituary appeared in the June issue of Scottish Birds (Vol 22, No 1).

## RESULTS OF THE BBS SURVEYS FOR CENTRAL REGION
*(Based on a comprehensive summary by NB)*

This year the bird report continues to make extensive use in the species accounts of results from the Breeding Birds Survey, these are in terms of the frequency of occurence of a species along linear transects in several habitat types. In 2000, 29 1x1 kilometre squares were surveyed, one less than 1999. Each square is usually visited twice in spring/summer, a total of 2 km on a set route is walked per visit and all birds noted in 200 m sections; a standardised habitat survey is done on another visit. In the main report I have presented selected results, calculated as birds per 10 km of habitat, for the major habitats where it is likely that the birds are breeding locally. For species that are scarce – say, one or less per 10 km – results may vary erratically from year to year.

Each square (sometimes half squares) and the birds noted in it have been attributed to one of four major habitats – Mountain and moorland (=moor), Conifers (woodland + wood/moorland edge), Farmland, Urban/suburban. Broadleaved woodland occurs mainly as copses in farmland whilst conifer woodland includes both young plantations and mature woods, thus "Conifers" figures may include species of scrub and moorland edge which are not found in mature plantations. Also, some urban squares may include bushy areas on the fringe of towns.

An average of 25 species were recorded per square (excluding four squares that were visited only once and one with numbers of non-breeding gulls and waders), but with great variation from five on high moorland to 35 on mixed farmland, numbers of individuals also varied widely from 59 to 620, average 318. The commonest species per habitat were: Moor – Meadow Pipit, Conifer – Chaffinch, Farmland – Starling, Urban – Starling. Species showing marked increases (40 % or greater) included Lapwing, Oystercatcher, Skylark, Whitethroat, Sedge Warbler, Starling and Goldfinch. Whinchat, Jay, Bullfinch and Siskin are now well below their long term means.

1999 contributors were: S. Agnew, MA, NB, W.R. Brackenridge, R. Bullman, DJC, P. Carter, RC, RD, R. Dalzeil, S. Davies, DE, J. Grainger, CJH, JN, DJ, DOE, R. Osborn, AT, MT, D. Redwood, SS, B. Urquhart, JW, T. Young, SZ.

## WILDFOWL REPORT 2000-2001

This report concerns the inland waters part of this area's Wetland Bird Survey (WEBS) organised by NB and is a condensed version of a fuller report by him.

WEBS is a monthly waterfowl census under the auspices of the British Trust for Ornithology (BTO) and the Wildfowl & Wetlands Trust (WWT), it runs from September to March inclusive though in this season only half the sites were counted in September and, due to foot and mouth restrictions, some February counts and all those in March were aborted. For this report 'wildfowl' includes divers, grebes, cormorants, herons, swans, geese (excluding Pink-footed and Greylag for which the WWT organises separate counts), ducks and rails.

This report covers the area occupied by the new local government councils of Stirling, Falkirk and Clackmannanshire (the 'region'). In total, 124 still water sites, 118 km of river and 16.1 km of canal were counted by 43 counters.

### Still Water Sites

Standing water in Central Region amounts to 7693 hectares or 2.9 % of the area.

The following table consists of matched monthly data for total wildfowl on 14 sites in the top 25. Those sites holding fed Mallard have been excluded.

| Month | 1997/8 | 1998/9 | 1999/0 | 2000/1 |
|---|---|---|---|---|
| September | 1756 | 1494 | 1605 | 1356 |
| October | 2454 | 2082 | 2812 | 1821 |
| November | 3037 | 2633 | 3257 | 3286 |
| December | 3396 | 2710 | 3386 | 3312 |
| January | 3332 | 2599 | 3045 | 3086 |
| February | 2940 | 2133 | 2244 | 2157 |
| March | 1930 | 1338 | 1334 | 1599 |
| Total | 18845 | 14989 | 17683 | 16617 |

This season's numbers are down 6 % on the previous largely due to the low figure for October.

Turning to individual sites, the top ten along with monthly averages are listed below:- (previous season's figures in brackets)

| | Site | Average | |
|---|---|---|---|
| 1. (1) | Gartmorn Dam | 534 | (530) |
| 2. (2) | Gart complex | 469 | (479) |
| 3. (8) | Loch Earn | 416 | (231) |
| 4. (3) | Lake of Menteith | 363 | (288) |
| 5. (9) | Vale of Coustry | 291 | (224) |
| 6. (4) | Airthrey Loch | 269 | (283) |
| 7. (6) | Loch Venachar | 253 | (249) |
| 8. (5) | Blairdrummond Park | 233 | (274) |
| 9. (7) | L.Dochart-Iubhair | 220 | (240) |
| 10. (18) | Kersiepow South Pond | 162 | (89) |

The above table excludes sites where Mallard are reared and released for shooting. Most sites showed little change in total numbers this season except for L.Earn which increased greatly.

## Linear Water Features: Rivers & Canals

This season coverage of the rivers length decreased slightly. The most favoured river was the Teith with 22 birds km$^{-1}$, closely followed by the Forth; canals scored at 5.1 km$^{-1}$.

WEBS contributors to these data, additional to report list were: B. Barker, M. Blunt, A. Boast, A. Downie, M. Ferguson, A. Hannah, M. Hardy, M. Kobs, R. Osborn, P. Series, D. Shenton, B. Urquhart, A. Wallace, H. Weir, M. White, T. Young.

## SYSTEMATIC LIST

Codes – S, F and C indicate records from Stirling, Falkirk and Clackmannanshire "Districts".

**\*RED-THROATED DIVER** *Gavia stellata (b,w)*
F    1 Blackness 26 Mar, 2 on 5 Nov & 10 Dec (MA DT). 3 Skinflats 17 Dec (GO). 1 Bo'ness 28 Oct 7 & 10 Dec (DMB).
S    Trossachs: noted at 3 sites from 28 Feb; juvenile seen 20 Jul (NB DJC).

**\*BLACK-THROATED DIVER** *Gavia arctica (b,w)*
F    1 Kinneil 23 Jan & 1 Blackness 30 Jan (MA).
S    Trossachs: noted at 3 sites 22 Mar to 16 Jul & 2 on 8th; nest at usual site failed due to drought (NB  DAC DJC).

**LITTLE GREBE** *Tachybaptus ruficollis (B,w)*
    WEBS max: 48 inland in Feb, 59 in Oct (NB).
F    At Skinflats 1 Jan to 22 Mar, 12 Sep to 25 Dec, max 8 on 21 Jan & 10 on 1 Dec (AA AB MA GO). 4 W.Mains Pond 18 Mar; Pr with 2Y St Helen's Loch (Bonnybridge) 1 Oct (MA).
C    2 Cambus Pools 12 Mar, 2 on 22 Sep & 3 on 8 Oct (AT CJH). 3 Gartmorn 29 Feb (AT).
S    Breeding season: 2 L.Watston 18 Mar & 2J on 19 Sep; Pr Carron Valley Res 15 Apr, Doune Ponds 25 Mar, probably bred Cambusmore  (CJH AKM DOE PWS). Max Gart 12 on 5 Oct; total 16 L.Lubnaig/Voil/Dochart in Dec (NB).

**GREAT CRESTED GREBE** *Podiceps cristatus (b,W)*
    WEBS totals: 20 Forth estuary in Sep (DMB); 42 inland in Mar (only 8 in Jan), 21 in Oct(NB).
F    23 Blackness 23 Jan, 27 on 5 Nov & 10 Dec (MA). Kinneil: 22 on 23 Jan, last 2 on 1 Apr; 3 on 19 Jul, 26 on 27 Aug, 29 on 16 Sep, max 37 on 23 Dec (AB GO DT). On 23 Mar, Prs in BP at Little Denny Res & Drumbowie Res; 2 ad + Juv Black Loch 12 Sep, last 1 on 15 Dec (NB). 1 L.Ellrig 20 Mar & 2 on 20 Sep (JN).
C    Gartmorn: 8 on 30 Jan, 6 on 13 Mar; 13 on 20 Nov, 1 on 18 Dec (AT).
S    13 Carron Valley Res 12 Mar, 4 Pr 15 Apr & 3 N on 25 May, last 1 on 22 Oct. Pr raised 2Y at Cocksburn Res & L.Watston (DAC AKM AT CJH). Pr + 3Y& Pr on nest Cambusmore 24 Jun (PWS). 2 Pr Lake of Menteith 29 Apr, 2Y on 1 Jul (DOE RAB). In BP in Mar at Blairdrummond, L.Venachar & L.Ard (DOE DJC NB).

**\*SLAVONIAN GREBE** *Podiceps auritus*
S    1 Carron Valley Res 22 Jul (AKM).

**\*FULMAR** *Fulmarus glacialis (p)*
F    Blackness: 2->E 4 Jun, 1 on 19 Aug & 5 Nov, 1->W on 10 & 24 Dec (MA). 1 Kinneil 19 Jul to 15 Oct (DT).

**MANX SHEARWATER** *Puffinus puffinus*
F    1 Kinneil 27 Aug (DT).

**\*GANNET** *Sula bassana (p)*
F    3->W Blackness 24 Sep, 3 Kinneil 10 Sep & 1 on 15th – all Juvs (MA GO AB).

**CORMORANT** *Phalacrocorax carbo (S,W)*
    WEBS max: 214 Forth Estuary in Jan & 176 in Oct (DMB). 37 inland in Mar &

110 in Dec (NB).
F     35 Carronmouth 4 Sep & 14 Kinneil on 19th (AB GO).
C     116 S.Alloa roost 28 Dec (AT).
S     16 Carron Valley Res 12 Mar (DAC). 1 Lake of Menteith 22 Aug & 17 on 1 Oct (NB DT).
GREY HERON  *Ardea cinerea (B,W)*
    WEBS max: 34 Forth Estuary in Sep (DMB). 97 inland in Jan, 128 in Dec (NB).
F     27 Airth 21 Feb (GO). 23 Skinflats (max) 17 Sep (MVB).
C     22 on lower Devon 15 Dec (GEL DE).
S     12 Blairdrummond 8 Mar (NB). 32 used nests Carrat-Nyadd 16 Jun (CJH).
*SPOONBILL  *Platalea leucorodia*
C     1 Cambus Pools 13 May, unfortunately did not stay long (W R Brackenridge).
MUTE SWAN  *Cygnus olor (B,W)*
    WEBS max: 36 Forth Estuary in Sep (DMB). 233 inland in Jan, 256 in Dec (NB).
F     8 Prs around Falkirk reared 33 Juv (MA). Max at Skinflats 32 in Jan, 25 in Feb, 33 in Mar, 41 in Apr; few late in year, 17 on 30 Dec (GO AB AA MVB DAC).
C     2 Prs Blackdevonmouth 11 May (DOE). 2 Prs + 8Y at Cambus Pools, Pr+2Y on river (CJH). 27 on floods at Alva 16 Nov & 10 Dec, with Whoopers 19-26 Nov; 28 Gartmorn 18 Dec (NB AT).
    22 Juv reared from 8 sites (NB CJH PWS DT). Max Lake of Menteith 30 on 19 Jan (NB). 33 Forthbank 27 Feb (AT). 10 with Whoopers by Devon at Blairlogie 14 Jan & 18 on 16 Feb (CJH).
WHOOPER SWAN  *Cygnus cygnus (W)*
    max inland (mainly WEBS): 209 in Dec – 12.3 % Juv, n = 155 (NB).
    Ringed adults, 15 Jan: 1 at Gogar ringed Iceland on 10/8/99; 1 at Gargunnock ringed as juv Martin Mere on 15/12/93 (NB).
F     9 ->W Blackness 5 Nov (DT). 95 Throsk 17 Nov (RD). 10 St Helen's Loch 10 Feb & 8 on 20 Nov, prob. pylon casualty on 19th (AA).
C     26 -> SW Cambus 5 Apr. Max with Mutes: 14 Blairlogie 14 Jan & 16 Feb, 42 Alva on 19 – 26 Nov (AT CJH). 80, with Greylags, in partly harvested cereal Cambus 3 Dec, *prob. the Nov herd from Throsk* (CJH).
S     L.Dochart: 67 on 20 Mar (PWS) – prob. spring passage since only 18 on 19 & 21 Mar & 10 in Jan-Feb, last 12 on 2 Apr (DOE); 26 on 11 Dec. 19 L.Venachar 30 Nov (DJC).
    Carse of Stirling: 47 on 15 Jan, 35 on 17 Mar (NB DR). 2 on 17 Sep (RC) *early for 1st of autumn – tame, ? injured, Ed;* 9 on 8 Oct was typical (DP); max 32 on 9 Dec (DAC).
PINK-FOOTED GOOSE  *Anser brachyrhynchus (W)*
    Considerable flocks reported throughout the lowland areas, in the absence of regular coordinated counts these are difficult to interpret. 2000 Blairdrummond Carse 15 Jan were probably extra to the 2000 Thornhill Carse on 17 Mar since 3420 on both areas 13 Feb, 3000 Thornhill Carse on 26 Feb & 4000 Lecropt on 4 Mar (NB MVB SS DT). In the east, 2160 Airth on 16 Jan & 3000 Skinflats on 26 Feb probably overlapped, and contributed to the later Alloa Inch records – 1000 on 2 Apr, 1670 on 23rd, still 25 on 10 May (MVB AS DMB). Max inland in Falkirk were 350 L.Ellrig 20 Mar & 313 Slamannan on 15 Dec (JN NB). Spring movement to north included 185 Bonnybridge on 29 Apr & 150 Bridge of Allan 5 & 7 May (MA CJH).
    The main arrival started with 21 Thornhill, 85 L.Watston and 37 -> SW Grangemouth on 19 Sep, 100 -> S Buchlyvie & 75 Kinneil on 23rd, 250 Thornhill on 24th and 200 Skinflats on 25th (SS CJH GO DAC DT DOE AB). On the Carse of Stirling numbers rapidly built to 4000 on 8 Oct, in the east 200 came in high

from the NW at Blackdevonmouth on 6 Oct (2000 there on 1 Nov) and there were 1450 at Skinflats on 8 Oct & 2750 on 12 Dec – 3910 on whole estuary (DP CJH DMB MVB).

*BEAN GOOSE  *Anser fabalis (W)*
F     At Carron Valley Res 46 on 21 Jan, 1st of autumn 16 on 13 Oct (GJB). 187 Slamannan 27 Oct (NB).

*WHITE-FRONTED GOOSE  *Anser albifrons* (w)
F     1 Skinflats 12 Feb (GO).
S     1 (Greenland race) Blairdrummond carse 15 Jan, with Pinkfeet & Greylags, & on 20 Feb (NB DT).

GREYLAG GOOSE  *Anser anser (b,W)*
Substantial flocks were noted mainly on Drip/Blairdrummond/Thornhill carse with 800 on 15 Jan, 590 on 13 Feb & 1000 on 18 Mar, last were 40 ->N at Killin on 16 Apr & 3 Skinflats on 29th (NB MVB PG PWS GO). The max further north was 154 G.Dochart 25 Mar (NB). The only "spring" numbers east of Stirling were 477 Slamannan 9 Jan & at L.Ellrig, 250 on 16 Jan & 200 on 13 Feb (NB JN). The 1st of autumn were early, 35->SE Skinflats on 4 Sep; 11 ->SSW Fallin on 6 Oct & 16 Skinflats on 13th, were more usual (AB RD GO). Few on Carse of Stirling until late autumn, max 400 on 29 Nov & 590 on 13 Dec (DR NB). None reported from north of area. In the east, noted on flooded stubble at Alva from 19 Nov (105) to end of year with max 212 on 10 Dec & 217 on 23rd. 45 at Fallin 28 Dec & Cambus on 29th pres. same flock (AT NB RD).

CANADA GOOSE  *Branta canadensis (b,W)*
WEBS max: 161 inland in Feb, 252 in Nov (NB).
F     max 25 Bonnybridge 15 Sep (MA).
S     Max early in year was 53 L.Venachar 20 Jan (NB). Autumn max was 118 Cambusmore 4 Nov (DOE), other notable records were 53 G.Finglas 10 Aug, 27 ->S Fallin 1 Oct & 36 Carron Valley Res on 22nd, 40 L.Coulter on 3 Nov, 73 Coustry (Blairdrummond) 13 Dec. Max on main Carse of Stirling only 7, Jan to Apr (DJC RD DAC IW NB DR GO). At Lecropt on 22 Feb, in 800 Pinkfeet, was a small Canada with rounded head & small beak, pale breast & light grey back – possibly a migrant of race *hutchinsii*, known to breed in Greenland (NB). Spring pairs at Lake of Menteith (11Y on 1 Jul), Thornhill, Cambusmore, Carron Valley Res (5Y). (RAB NB PWS DAC).

*BARNACLE GOOSE  *Branta leucopsis (w)*
F     7 Skinflats 30 Sep, 36 on 1 Oct & 70 on 8th (DMB MA).
C     3 Alloa Inches 2 Apr & 4 on 23rd (DMB).
S     46 ->SW Kinbuck & 6 Fallin ->E 30 Sep, then 37 ->W 1 Oct (RD DT –*NB Skinflats records, Ed*). 1 Kippen 20 & 27 Feb, 2 Balfron 23 Feb – all feeding with Pinkfeet/Greylag flocks (DAC).

*BRENT  GOOSE  *Branta bernicla*
F     1 dark bellied adult Skinflats 8-13 Feb (GO AB).

SHELDUCK  *Tadorna tadorna (b,W)*
WEBS max: 783 Forth Estuary in Feb & 2940 in Aug (DMB).
F     Moult flock at Kinneil totalled 2940 on 19 Aug; 920 on 28 Oct. Skinflats: 325 on 16 Jan, 700 on 4 Sep & 734 on 17th (DMB MVB AB). Inland, 1 Black Loch 19 Dec (NB) - *1st record & unusual date, Ed.*
C     97 Tullibody Inch 25 Mar (DMB). 8 pairs Blackdevonmouth 8 May (CJH).
S     11 Cambuskenneth in Feb were highest up Forth (AT). 2 L.Venachar 19 Dec (NB) –*1st record & unusual date, Ed.*

WIGEON  *Anas penelope (b,W)*
WEBS max: 1087 Forth Estuary in Jan & 1040 in Dec (DMB), 638 inland in Jan &

1024 in Dec (NB).

F  215 Blackness 3 Jan & 150 on5 Nov, 50 Carriden on 16th (MA DT DMB). Kinneil: max 300 on 6 Feb, 200 to13 Mar, 32 on 1 Apr; 110 on 23 Sep, 570 on 28 Oct (DT GO AB DMB). Skinflats: 223 on 11 Mar, 13M on 16 Apr; 12 on 4 Sep, 47 on 11 Nov & 99 on 14 Dec (AB GO). 40 Lathallan 26 Nov (JW).

C  220 Alloa Inches 25 Mar, 250 on 13 Nov & 562 on 28 Dec (DMB RD AT). 200 on Devon, Alva, 28 Feb. Max Gartmorn 63 on 20 Nov (GEL AT).

S  Gart Lochs (Cambusmore): 409 on 11 Jan; 100 on 10 Aug, 300 on 28 Sep to 460 on 12 Dec. 130 L.Dochart 17 Feb & 127 on 14 Nov; 136 L.Venachar 19 Dec (NB DOE PWS DJC). Max on the upper Forth between the Teith and Gargunnock 356 in Feb, still 307 in mid-Mar (RC PG DR).

GADWALL  *Anas strepera*

F  Pr Skinflats 5 Mar (MA). Pr Kinneil 10 Sep (GO).

C  Gartmorn: 3(2M) 30 Jan & 5(3M) on 29 Feb;  M on 22 Oct, 4(1M) on 20 Nov & Pr to 28 Dec (AT).

S  M L.Mahaick 16 Mar, M Lake of Menteith 3 Dec (NB).

TEAL  *Anas crecca (B,W)*

WEBS max: 1021 Forth Estuary in Jan & 1793 in Dec (DMB). 986 inland in Jan, 1125 in Nov (NB).

F  Kinneil: 530 on 16 Jan, 1175 on 10 Dec. 236 Carronmouth 6 Feb. Skinflats: 134 on 16 Apr, 10 on 16 Jun, 18 on 30 Aug. Inland max 71 Carronshore 16 Jan (DMB MVB GO AB).

C  On Devon: 84 Alva-Dolla in Jan/Feb, 136 Kersiepow 16 Nov (GEL DE NB). Max Gartmorn Dam 49 on 18 Dec (AT). 24 Cambus Pools 16 Apr & 5 on 6 Jul. 4 Blackdevonmouth Marshes in Jun & 2 in Jul (DAC CJH).

S  280 on upper Forth in Feb (RC SE). 130 on tidal Forth above Fallin 19 Nov (DJ). 89 Blackwater Marshes 20 Jan (CJH). 101 Blairdrummond 5 Oct, 214 Gart 9 Nov (NB). 3 Flanders Moss 30 Jun & 100 on 2 Nov, 30 Thornhill 1 Sep (DP SS). Pr + F upper G.Buckie 15 Apr (DT).

MALLARD  *Anas platyrhynchos  (B,W)*

WEBS max: 569 Forth Estuary in Jan & 354 in Dec (DMB), 2358 inland in Jan & 3161 in Dec (NB). 8 Broods had 59 Y (MA AT).

F  184 Skinflats 16 Jan, 133 on 12 Dec (MVB). 299 Kinneil 16 Jan (DMB).

C  348 Gartmorn 18 Dec (AT). 3 broods Blackdevonmouth 16 Jun (CJH).

S  253 Airthrey 16 Jan & 291 on 19 Nov (MK). 226 L.Venachar 20 Jan. 282 Blairdrummond (Coustry) 5 Oct & 316 Safari Pond 13 Dec (NB).

PINTAIL  *Anas acuta (W)*

F  Skinflats/Carronmouth max 89 on 2 Jan, 66 on 14 Feb, last 4 on 27 Apr & 1 on 4 May; 2 on 3 Sep, 86 on 28 Dec. Few at Kinneil, last 2 on 25 Mar; 1st autumn on 4 Sep, max 24 on 15 Oct (MVB GO AB DMB DT).

C  Pr Cambus 12 Mar & M on 17th (CJH AT).

S  M Fallin 21 Dec (RD).

Area Summary

| Jan | Feb | Mar | Apr | - | Aug | Sep | Oct | Nov | Dec |
|-----|-----|-----|-----|---|-----|-----|-----|-----|-----|
| 89  | 72  | 6   | 4   |   | 0   | 17  | 35  | 45  | 87  |

SHOVELER  *Anas clypeata (p)*

F  Kinneil: from 8 Aug, 5 on 10 Sep & 12 on 15 Oct to 4 on 23 Dec. 3 Skinflats 4 Jul & 1 on 1 Nov. 1 Carronshore 16 Sep (DMB DT GO AB IH ).

C  2M Cambus Pools 3 May, 3 on 18 Jul; 1 on 8 Oct. 2 Pr Blackdevonmouth 15 Apr, Pr on 11 May (AT MVB CJH DOE).

S  1 Fallin 5 Oct & 21 Dec (RD).

POCHARD   *Aythya ferina (W)*
WEBS max: 185 inland in Jan, 155 in Nov (NB).
F       8 St Helen's Loch 1 Oct (MA).
C       28 Gartmorn 30 Jan, 19 on 20 Nov(AT).
S       62 L.Ard 20 Jan & 39 on 19 Dec. 19 L.Lubnaig 17 Feb & 20 L.Venachar on 28th.
27 Coustry 25 Jan, 45 Lake of Menteith & 13 Cambusmore 9 Nov (NB). 15
Carron Valley Res 15 Jan & 23 on 22 Oct (DAC).

TUFTED DUCK   *Aythya fuligula (B,W)*
WEBS max: 354 inland in Jan, 662 in Dec (NB).
F       32 Black Loch 12 Sep (NB). Max 9 Skinflats Jan/Feb, last 2 on 28 Apr; a few
autumn from 12 Sep (GO AB).
C       52 Gartmorn 30 Jan & 306 on 20 Nov (AT). 3 Cambus 15 Jul (CJH).
S       93 Coustry 25 Jan & 35 on 13 Dec. 56 Carron Valley Res 19 Sep, 77 Lake of
Menteith 9 Nov (NB DAC). 30 Gart 24 Jun;  F+7Y L.Watston 2 Jul & F+6Y
L.Dochart on 26th (PWS CJH).

SCAUP   *Aythya marila (w)*
F       Kinneil: Pr on 30 Apr & 16 Sep, 3 on 23rd & 1 on 30th. Skinflats: 1 on 19 Jan;
from 17 Sep to 11 Nov, max 7 on 19 Sep (DT AB DMB MVB GO).
S       1 on Forth at Frew 31 Jan (DR).

*EIDER   *Somateria mollissima (w)*
F       Blackness: M on 23 Jan & F on 30th, 3(2M) on 26 Mar; Pr on 26 Nov & M on 24
Dec (MA). 3M Kinneil 23 Jan & 2 on 2 &16 Apr. 1 Carronmouth 1 Jan & 3 on 7
Apr. (MA DMB DT GO).

GOLDENEYE   *Bucephula clangula (W)*
WEBS max: 107 Forth Estuary in Jan & 40 in Oct (DMB). 644 inland in Feb, 487
in Dec (NB). Few summering birds & late autumn return – 1st on 5 Oct, eclipse
M at Coustry.
F       36 Carronshore 16 Jan & 13 Feb (AB MA). 43 Skinflats 19 Feb, last 4 on 27 Apr;
30 on 16 Nov (GO AA). 52 Black Loch 21 Mar (NB).
C       33 Kennetpans 16 Jan. 51 Alloa Inches 28 Dec. 73 Gartmorn 18 Mar & 89 on 18
Dec (CJH AT). 115 on lower Devon (Tillicoultry to Cambus) in Feb (GEL PD
KW). Devonmouth: last 2F on 13 Apr; 2 on 5 Aug & 1 on 18th (AT DAC CJH).
S       F in nestbox L.Tay, eggs deserted 4 Jun (PWS). 117 on Forth, Fallin-Stirling in
Feb, 55 Forthbank 16 Dec DJ AT). 46 Lake of Menteith 19 Jan. 47 L.Venachar 28
Feb & 29 Mar. 53 L.Ard 29 Mar. 50 L.Dochart/Iubhair 15 Jan & 41 on 11 Dec (NB
PWS). 29 Carron Valley Res 15 Jan & 18 on 16 Dec (DAC).

*SMEW   *Mergus albellus (w)*
S       L.Dochart/Iubhair: M on 12 Jan to 25  Mar. M on 26 Dec (PWS NB DAC).

RED-BREASTED MERGANSER   *Mergus serrator (B,W)*
21 Forth Estuary in Feb & 32 in Oct (DMB).
F       Skinflats: 21 on 6 Feb, 14 on 7 Apr, 7 on 7 May; 14 on 10 Oct & 21 on 30th. 19
Kinneil 23 Jan & 35 on 15 Sep & 15 Oct. 12 Bo'ness 23 Jan (MVB GO AB MA DT
AS).
C       M on Devon at Tullibody 17 Feb & 14 Mar (KW).
S       2 Pr L.Katrine 29 Mar (NB). Pr+8Y Killin 2 Aug. Pr L.Dochart 6 Nov - late (PWS)

GOOSANDER   *Mergus merganser (B,W)*
WEBS max: 134 inland in Jan, 150 in Dec. 16 on estuary in Oct (NB DMB). 1st
Ms in autumn were 23 & 28 Oct (Forthbank, R.Carron, Cambus), 18 Nov
(Carronshore) (AT DAC IH)
F       8 Skinflats 19 Sep, 20 on 10 Oct (GO AB). 15 R.Carron (Larbert) 17 Dec (MA).
C       R.Devon: 6 at Cambus Aug 5 (DAC). 26 Dollar-Cambus 15 Dec (DE GEL KW).

S    22 on Forth, Fallin to Teith, in Dec (RD AT MB). 11 on Allan Water (Dunblane-Kinbuck) in Nov (AW). 6 prs L.Katrine 29 Mar (NB).

*RUDDY DUCK *Oxyura jamaicensis (w)*
C    Gartmorn: Pr on 29 Feb, 3(2M) on 29 Mar (AT).

*HONEY BUZZARD *Pernis apivorus*
S    1 Doune 21 Jul (DOE KD).

RED KITE *Milvus milvus*
The RSPB/Scottish Natural Heritage re-establishment scheme continues with a max winter roosts of 31 on 9 Feb & 45 on 10 Dec. Seven broods attempted, 5 pairs raised 10Y. 20 birds released in Aug in last phase of the scheme. A female was found poisoned (DOE). Please try to note wing tag colours on any bird you may see, Ed.
Around Doune/Lecropt there were 3 on 22 Jan, 4 on 13 Feb, 1 or 2 Mar to Oct (1 flew off with meat chunk from factory at BoA) 4 on 4 Nov & 5 on 10 Dec. 3 Callendar 16 Mar (DT AT DMB DK PWS CJM DK NB). 1 Carron Valley Res 21 Apr & 15 May (GJB). Pair in Trossachs Mar to May. 1 flew into Clacks from Castlehill Res on 17 Mar (DE).

*MARSH HARRIER *Circus aeruginosus*
S    F Thornhill 13 May (SS).

HEN HARRIER *Circus cyaneus (b, w)*
7 males and 9 Ringtails noted, omitting repeated records.
F    M Skinflats 18 & 27 Feb (GO).
S    Pairs & singles on Carse of Stirling/Flanders Moss 15 Jan to 6 Feb and 26 Aug to 4 Dec. Also on surrounding hill ground & Strathallan, but no records between 18 Mar & 4 Sep. 1 Carron Valley 21 Apr to 24 Jun (SS DJC DT MVB DOE KD JW DP IW MA GJB).

*GOSHAWK *Accipiter gentilis*
S    1 Airthrey 12 Feb, 31 Mar & 21 May (DMB). 1 Doune 26 Feb (DOE).

SPARROWHAWK *Accipiter nisus (B,W)*
BBS reports 1 per 10 km in "Urban"; surprisingly, none this year from conifers – however, there is great yearly variation in the apparently preferred habitat.
Many records throughout area, mainly Jan/Feb & Nov/Dec; seen in gardens at Buchlyvie, Strathyre (chased Chaffinches), Stirling, Tillicoultry, Polmont. Chased Mistle Thrushes at Cambus (DAC DJC CJM AT JW). Few noted in midsummer when it is presumably secretive. 3 prs displaying Braes of Doune 25 Mar (DOE). Raised 2Y Skinflats (GO AB).

BUZZARD *Buteo buteo (B,W)*
As breeding bird: widespread S & C, scarce F.
F    Ad with 2 Juv by Carron west of Larbert 27 Aug – 5 there on 13 Feb (MA). At Torwood & Polmont (6 on 19 Feb) all year. 2 Wallacebank Feb-Apr & Nov (AB JW AS). Possible migrants Skinflats 8 Apr & 7 Oct (GO DAC).
C    Widespread through year. Max: 8 Tillicoultry 25 Mar & 5 on 15 Apr, 5 Blackdevonmouth 16 Apr (DAC AT DMB).
S    2 AoT Lanrick 29 Apr, 12 AoT Braes of Doune reared 24Y (group 15 Argaty 15 Nov). Other large groups in breeding range were 12 Doune 25 Mar & 8 Blairdrummond on 26th, 8 Airthrey 28 Apr, 4 Cambusbarron on 13 Mar, 5 Strathyre 22 Aug, 4 Callander 20 Oct, 6 Doune (Row) 13 Dec (DOE DMB AS DJC NB).

GOLDEN EAGLE *Aquila chrysaetos (b,w)*
S    8 territories checked, 8 occupied by pairs. Only 2 successful, reared 2Y (PSA).

OSPREY *Pandion haliaetus*
S    1st seen 8 Apr, last 31 Aug (DAC KD). Seven pairs laid, of which 6 reared 14

young – twice number for 1999; also one late territory (DOE). 1 Lecropt 5 Aug, summer records from Carron Valley Res, last 3 on 23 Aug (DT AKM JNW).

KESTREL   *Falco tinnunculus (B,W)*
Difficult to make significant observations, hence greatly underrecorded. BBS shows overall as frequent as Sparrowhawk; 6 per 100 km in farmland.
F   Through year at Skinflats (AB GO).
S   Pr + 3 Juv Doune 6 Aug (DOE).

MERLIN   *Falco columbarius (b?,w)*
F   1 by R.Carron, Camelon, 13 Mar & 8 Oct (MA).
S   M G.Finglas 14 May, 1 G.nam Meann (Finglas) 29 Aug (DJC). 3 Carse of Stirling Jan/Feb & 5 Oct-Dec. M with small bird Blairlogie 15 Jan. 1 Kinbuck 25 Mar. 1 Braes of Doune 10 Aug (DOE NB RN MVB SS KD).

PEREGRINE   *Falco peregrinus (B,W)*
F   5 coastal records Jan, Dec – chased Redshank at Blackness. 2 over Falkirk Aug, Oct (AB MA).
S&C   19 territories checked, 14 pairs & 2 single. 11 successful pairs reared 24 Y (minimum, PSA). Aberfoyle nest on public CCTV (DOE). 1 on low ground Feb & 12 Aug-Dec. Records in breeding areas Mar-Nov. Seen over freshly killed Black-headed Gull, stooped at Crows, Jackdaws, ducks flushed by observer, Teal – stoop aborted due to near collision with deerfence (DJC DAC DP MA RD SS AS).

RED GROUSE   *Lagopus lagopus (B,W)*
Generally under-recorded. BBS shows 6 per 10 km on moorland.
S   4 sites in Gargunnocks-Kippen Muir, max 13 Cringate 13 Jan (GO NB). Heard Flanders Moss 23 May. (SS).

BLACK GROUSE   *Tetrao tetrix  (B,W)*
S   25 lek sites totalling 82 Ms (15 % decrease over 1999 – nb data published in 1999 report was based on incomplete sample); one lek visited by hybrid M Black Grouse/Capercaillie, as 1999, & also, on 13 Apr, by a bird with body colour and tail shape as Red Grouse but white mark on wing and white undertail – presumably a hybrid with Black Grouse (DJC). 10 Ardeonaig (L.Tay) 10 Mar (PWS).

CAPERCAILLIE   *Tetrao urogallus*
S   no records received

GREY PARTRIDGE   *Perdix perdix (B,W)*
Coveys increase going east from the central carse of Stirling into Falkirk.
F   6 Blackness 18 Jan (AS). 3 Kinneil 8 Jan & 6 on 4 Nov. 6 Skinflats 1 Jan, 9 on 6 Aug & 11 on 3 Nov. 12 Carronshore 17 Sep( GO AB). 9 Camelon 1 Feb & 16 nearby 28/29 Sep (MA). 30 Lathallan 26 Nov & 26 on 17 Dec (JW).
C   12 Kennetpans 5 Feb (MA).
S   6 Drip Carse 27 Nov, 11 Blairdrummond 31 Dec & 30 Lecropt 4 Nov, 13 Cambuskenneth 2 Jan, 16 Fallin 1 Oct to 9 Nov (IW MVB DT AT RD).

PHEASANT   *Phasianus colchicus (B,W)*
Abundant (usually by releases) on fields next to keepered estates.
F   Pr Skinflats to end Mar, M to end year (AB GO).

WATER RAIL   *Rallus aquaticus (w)*
F   2 Kinneil 30 Sep (DMB). Skinflats: 2 on 20 Jan, from 17 Mar to 29 Aug, max 2 on 17 Mar & 1 Apr (AB GO). 1 Falkirk (W.Mains Pond) 16 Jan & 16 Dec (MA).
C   1 Cambus Pools 15 Jul & 18 Aug (CJH). 1 Tullibody Inch  22 Aug, 2 on 1 Sep & 3 on 12th (DMB MVB).
S   1 Killin on 14th (NB).

*CORNCRAKE Crex crex*
S    1 calling in hayfield at edge of west Flanders Moss (Collymoon) 21/22 Jun (SZ).
     1 calling by Dochart (Auchlyne) 8 Jul (*per* SZ).
MOORHEN *Gallinula chloropus (B,W)*
     WEBS max: 132 inland in Jan & 201 in Nov (NB).
F    17 Skinflats 16 Jan & 18 on 20 Feb (MVB MA). Max on Union Canal 66 on 17 Sep
     (JW PD JN). 28 Callendar Park 18 Jan & 24 on 17 Nov (AA).
C    17 Alva-Dollar in Jan (GEL DE). Max 10 Cambus Pools 20 Feb. Pr+4Y
     Blackdevonmouth 22 Aug (CJH).
S    Airthrey: 15 on 12 Mar & 12 on 18 Dec (MK) Pr +2Y+Juv Viewforth Pond 12 Jul;
     Pr +5 small Y Fallin 11 Oct – late date (JNW). At Killin marshes from 11 Feb to
     5 Nov, 4Y in Jul (PWS).
COOT *Fulica atra (B,W)*
     WEBS max: 603 inland in Jan & 361 in Nov (NB).
F    30 Callendar Park 18 Jan (AA). 26 Little Denny Res 9 Jan (NB).
C    15 Cambus Pools 20 Feb, only 2 in May. Pr+4Y Blackdevonmouth 17 Jul (CJH).
     81 Gartmorn Dam 30 Jan, 129 on 20 Nov (AT).
S    Airthrey: 69 on 16 Jan, 28 on 18 Dec (MK). 8 AoT L.Watston 2 Jul (CJH). 237 Lake
     of Menteith 19 Jan, 106 on 3 Dec. 52 Gart Nov/Dec (NB).
OYSTERCATCHER *Haematopus ostralegus (B,W)*
     200 on Forth Estuary in Feb & 190 in Sep (DMB).
     Apart from 2 Airthrey on 2 Feb & 1 Thornhill 2nd Feb, spring return inland in
     mid-February: Craigforth 13th, G.Lochay 19th, Dunblane & Kippen 20th (DMB
     SS MVB DT DOE DAC).
F    103 Blackness 30 Jan & 120 on 10 Dec; 151 Kinneil 16 Jan, 110 on 30 Jul. (MA
     DMB DT).
C    Pr Blackdevonmouth May/Jun (CJH).
S    In Feb: 500 Craigforth 13th & 480 on 17th, 333 Blairdrummond on 22nd. 200
     Gart 17 Mar (DT MVB CJH NB PWS).
RINGED PLOVER *Charadrius hiaticula (b,W)*
     44 Forth Estuary in Jan & 29 in Sep (DMB).
F    30 Kinneil 16 Jan & 27 on 27 Feb, 33 on 10 Sep. Blackness: 22 on 27 Feb, 28 on 19
     Aug & 22 on 5 Nov; 21 Bo'ness 28 Dec. 14 Skinflats 16 Jan, poor spring passage
     except 22 on 6 Jun (DMB MA AB DT AS MVB GO).
S    Pr Cambusmore 17 Mar (PWS). 1 Kippen Muir 23 Apr, Pr+1Y Finglas Res 1 Jun.
     1 Carron Valley Res 2 Jul & 1 on 3 Sep (DAC DJC AKM).
GOLDEN PLOVER *Pluvialis apricaria (B,W)*
     Few breeding records. 1310 on Forth estuary in October (DMB).
F    Blackness: 93 on 6 Aug were 1st of autumn, 175 on 19th (MA DT). Skinflats: 184
     on 21 Jan, 280 on 17 Sep & 390 on 12 Dec. 300 Airth on 18 & 23 Oct were eclipsed
     by 1310 Bellsdyke (N of Skinflats) on 29th. 230 Kinneil 3 & 10 Dec. (GO MVB
     CJH AB).
S    2 Dochart hills (B.n.Imirean) 22 Mar (*per* PWS). 2 pr G.Ogle 31 May (DOE). 3
     upper G.Buckie 15 Apr (DT).
GREY PLOVER *Pluvialis squatarola (W)*
F    Scarce on estuary. Skinflats: 8 on 2 Jan, max 14 on 11 Oct (MVB GO). 2 Blackness
     16 Apr (MA).
LAPWING *Vanellus vanellus (B,W)*
     1314 on Forth Estuary in Jan & 3221 in Dec (DMB).
F    235 Bo'ness 13 Oct (AS). Skinflats: 800 on 2 Jan, 1070 on 17 Sep & 1340 on 29 Oct.
     Kinneil: 1500 on 6 Feb & 800 on 1 Oct. 800 Higgins Neuk 18 Oct. (MVB AB MA
     DT CJH).

8 AoT (+ Juvs) Blackdevonmouth 17 Jun. 190 Alva 1 Oct. 460 Tullibody Inch 30 Jul & 1100 on 14 Aug. (CJH AT).

S   Spring return: 250 Lecropt 13 Feb & 400 on 17th. 5 AoT Flanders Moss set-aside 12 May, 30 AoT Braes of Doune (Severie) on 18th & 7 AoT Doune Ponds on 23rd. 100 BoA 6 Jul was early post-nesting flock; 400 Cambusmore 10 Aug. (DT CJH DOE LJM PWS).

KNOT   *Calidris canutus  (W)*
3000 Forth Estuary in Jan & 3550 in Dec (DMB).
F   3000 Kinneil 16 Jan. Skinflats: 1st of autumn 1 on 8 Jul, 100 on 10 Sep; 2550 on 12 Dec fed on mudflats, roosted Kinneil. 2500 Bo'ness & 750 Blackness on 10 Dec (DMB GO AB DT MVB MA).

*SANDERLING   *Calidris alba (p)*
F   1 Skinflats 1 Aug (GO). 2 Kinneil 10 Sep (DMB).

*LITTLE STINT   *Calidris minutus*
F   1 Kinneil 23 Sep (DT).

CURLEW SANDPIPER   *Calidris ferruginea  (p)*
F   1 Kinneil 10 Sep & 2 on 15th. Skinflats (all immatures): 9 on 29 Aug, 2 on 15-17 Sep (DMB AB GO MVB).
Area Summary (half monthly)

| Aug | Sep |
|-----|-----|
| 0 9 | 3 4 |

DUNLIN   *Calidris alpina  (b?,W)*
9072 Forth Estuary in Jan & 10,015 in Dec (DMB).
6000 Kinneil 16 Jan; 1st of autumn 4 ad on 16 Jul. Skinflats: 3650 on 2 Jan & 3400 on 6 Feb; 50 on 18 Sep, 6900 on 12 Dec (DMB DT MVB AB).

RUFF   *Philomachus pugnax  (p)*
F   Skinflats: 1st of autumn 26 Jul, 4 on 15 Aug to 8 on 17 Sep, 1 on 30 Nov. Kinneil: 1 on 19 Aug, max 4 on 10 Sep (GO AB DT MVB ).
C   4 Tullibody Inch on 22 Aug & 1 on 1 Sep (DMB).
Area Summary (half monthly)

| Jul | Aug | Sep | Oct | Nov |
|-----|------|------|------|-----|
| 0 1 | 4 11 | 5 9 | 2 0 | 0 1 |

JACK SNIPE   *Lymnocryptes minimus  (w)*
F   1 Camelon 13 Feb. 2 Kinneil 22 Jan & 5 on 6 Feb; 8 on 4 Nov & 2 on 12 Dec. 1 Grangemouth 28 Oct. 1 Lathallan 29 Dec (MA DK DT GO DMB JW).
C   1 by Devon at Alva 15 Jan (GEL).
S   1 Thornhill 1 & 22 Oct (SS). 3 Flanders Moss 10 Nov & 1 on 28th (DP). 4 Lecropt 16 Dec (DT).

SNIPE   *Gallinago gallinago  (B,W)*
Probably under-recorded in breeding season but may have decreased (Ed).
F   Kinneil 13 on 19 Jan & 34 on 4 Nov. 22 Skinflats on 26 Jan & 19 on saltmarsh 5 Nov. 19 Grangemouth 28 Oct (GO AB DMB). 21 Bonnybridge 9 Jan, 15 West Mains Pond 19 Feb & 20 on 18 Mar (MA).
C   28 Gartmorn Dam 29 Feb (AT). 12 on Devon, Dollar-Alva, in Mar (DE GEL).
S   18 on upper Forth 16 Jan (SE PG). 20 Cambuskenneth 5 Feb (AT). In Apr-Jun at Thornhill, Flanders Moss, Braes of Doune (Severie, 6 displaying), G.Buckie, Earls Hill. 17 Flanders Moss 13 Sep. 29 Coustry 5 Oct, 24 Thornhill (Hillhead Pond) 3 Dec & 20 Lecropt on 16th. (SS DP DOE DT NB).

WOODCOCK   *Scolopax rusticola  (B,W)*
Under-recorded (Ed).
Roding in May/Jun at Invertrossachs, Blackwater Marshes, Kilbryde (2),

Dunblane. Oct-Dec records from Daldorn, Finglas, Cardross, Flanders Moss, Dunblane, Polmont. (DAC DJC DP NB MVB JW).

BLACK-TAILED GODWIT  *Limosa limosa (W)*

F    The max site count was 83 Skinflats 17 November; the whole estuary WEBS count in January found 75, which suggests that the higher totals of Kinneil +Skinflats in early January and, possibly, early October were due to double counting of birds that moved between the two sites. Numbers decreased in late May and there were few until early September. The only records from other sites were single birds at Cambus Pools, Tullibody Inch and Blackdevonmouth June to September. (GO AB DMB MVB et al)

Site Summary (half monthly)

| | Jan | Feb | Mar | Apr | May | Jun | Jul | Aug | Sep | Oct | Nov | Dec |
|---|---|---|---|---|---|---|---|---|---|---|---|---|
| Knnl | 75 37 | 45 | | 2 72 | | | 2 | 26 49 | 66 35 | 78 44 | 20 | 23 7 |
| Skn | 40 57 | | 75 | 72 67 | 54 54 | 54 9 | 1 | 16 6 | 15 20 | 21 30 | 61 83 | 15 |

BAR-TAILED GODWIT  *Limosa lapponica (W)*

    250 Forth Estuary in Feb & 140 in Dec (DMB).

F    240 Kinneil 2 Jan, last 30 Blackness on 30 Apr (MVB MA). lst of autumn 4 Kinneil 27 Aug (DT).

C    1 Tullibody Inch 1 Sep (DMB).

WHIMBREL  *Numenius phaeopus (p)*

F    In spring from 24 Apr to 7 May. 1st of autumn, 8 Skinflats on 19 Jul (flying W), last 10 Oct ( GO  AB MA).

S    2 ->N Lake of Menteith 7 May (RAB).

Area Summary (half monthly)

| Apr | May | Jul | Aug | Sep | Oct |
|---|---|---|---|---|---|
| 2 | 5 | 8 | 3 10 | | 1 |

CURLEW  *Numenius arquata  (B,W)*

    1055 on Forth estuary in Jan & 1059 in Sep (DMB).

F    250 Blackness 18 Jan & 272 on 6 Feb. 470 Skinflats 16 Jan, still 200 on 1 Mar; 442 on 12 Dec. 325 Kinneil 2 Jul & 700 on 10 Sep. (AS MA MVB GO DMB DT).

C    321 Kennetpans 16 Jan & 130 on 28 Oct; Cambus / Alloa Inches: 213 on 20 Feb & 190 on 17 Mar; 200 on 28 Dec. 2 AoT Blackdevonmouth (CJH AT).

S    Spring return Thornhill 1 Mar, 65 Lecropt on 4th & 120 on 11th, 35 on Thornhill Carse on 17th (SS DT DR MVB).

SPOTTED REDSHANK  *Tringa erythropus (p)*

F    Kinneil: lst of autumn 3 Sep, 2 to 28 Oct, 1 to end of year (GO DMB DT).

REDSHANK  *Tringa totanus (B,W)*

    1863 Forth Estuary in Jan & 2317 on Dec (DMB).

    lst spring return 13 February at Kildean, then in March: R.Devon & upper Forth on 12th, Gart on 16th, Kippen Muir on 21st, Killin on 30th (D&B GEL RC NB DAC PWS).

F    275 Bo'ness 13 Oct (AS). Skinflats: 765 on 2 Jan; 617 on 17 Sep & 570 on 12 Dec. Kinneil: 1142 on 16 Jan; 400 on 30 Jul & 920 on 28 Oct (MVB DMB DT).

C    3 AoT Blackdevonmouth in May, 2 anxious prs in Jun (CJH). In midwinter 1 on Devon at Tillicoultry on 15 Dec (DE).

S    6 AoT Braes of Doune (Severie) 18 May, 1 AoT Blackwater Marshes on 11th (DOE DJC).

GREENSHANK  *Tringa nebularia  (p)*

F    Skinflats: regular, max 3, from 1 Jan to 16 Apr; autumn from 20 Aug to 10 Oct (max 3 on 15 Sep); 1 from 17 Nov to 27 Dec. 1st Kinneil 30 Jul, 3 on 19 Aug, 5 on 3-10 Sep, 1 on 10 & 12 Dec (AB GO MA DT DMB MVB).

C    6 Tullibody Inch 1 Sep & 1 on 12 Nov (DMB).

S       1 Carron Valley Res 22 Jul (AKM). 1 Kilbryde 7 to 10 Aug, 1 Kelty Water 15 Sep
        (DP DAC).
        Area Summary (half monthly, autumn passage)
        Jul     Aug    Sep    Oct   Nov
        0  2    3  6   14  5   1  0   1  1

GREEN SANDPIPER  *Tringa ochropus  (p)*
F       2 on Carron (Larbert) 12 & 27 Mar. 2 Skinflats 28 Mar, 1 on 5 to 18 Apr. 1 Kinneil
        19 Aug. (MA AB GO DT DMB).
C       1 by Devon at Alva 12 Mar (GEL).1 Blackdevonmouth 11 Aug to 3 Sep, 2 on 5
        Dec (CJH DMB).

*WOOD  SANDPIPER  *Tringa glareola*
S       1 on flooded stubble at Thornhill 24 Sep (SS DOE DR).

COMMON SANDPIPER  *Tringa hypoleucos (B)*
        Spring return in April:, L.Tay & Blackdevonmouth on 16th, Kippen 21st, Larbert
        & G.Lochay 23rd (PWS DMB DAC MA DT).
F       1 Skinflats 30 Jun & 8 Jul (GO). Kinneil: from 2 Jul to 27 Aug, max 4 on 30 Jul
        (DT).
C       At Blackdevonmouth from 17 Jul, max 7 on 29th. Cambus-Tullibody Inch: 30 Jul
        (max 8 on 30th) to 1 Sep, late bird 12 Nov (CJH AT DMB). Last on Devon at
        Tillicoultry 22 Sep (DE).

Estuary autumn totals :     Jul      Aug      Sep
                            2  19     4  2     1  1

TURNSTONE  *Arenaria interpres  (W)*
F       Blackness: Jan to 16 Apr, max 19 on 3 Jan. 20 ->W Bo'ness 8 Apr  (MA). 6
        Skinflats 29 Jul (GO). 10 Carriden 10 Dec (DMB).

*POMARINE SKUA  *Stercorarius pomarinus*
F       1 Kinneil 28 Oct (DMB).

*ARCTIC  SKUA  *Stercorarius parasiticus  (p)*
F       1 Skinflats 4 Sep, chased Black-headed Gulls. Kinneil: 3 on 27 Aug & 23 Sep, 1
        on 1 Oct. Singles Blackness 23 Sep, 1 Oct (chased Sandwich Terns), 5 & 26 Nov
        (AB DT MA).

GREAT  SKUA  *Catharacta skua*
F       1 Kinneil 15 Oct (DT).

*MEDITERRANEAN GULL  *Larus melanocephalus*
S       Adult in winter plumage at Fallin 26 Dec (RD HC). First record for area (regular
        in outer Firth of Forth). Full description supplied; in summary: Seen floating
        down river with Black-headed and Common Gulls, telescope views to 70 m.
        White primaries conspicuous at 300 m. Slightly smaller than Common and
        larger than Black-headed Gull, head and neck heavier than latter and
        upperparts slightly paler grey; bill thicker, mainly bright red with paler,
        yellowish tip and blackish band across gonys; tops of legs visible and dark red.
        Dark streaking round eyes formed mask with white crescents above and below
        eyes.

*LITTLE  GULL  *Larus minutus*
F       1 Ad Skinflats 26 Nov (DMB).

BLACK-HEADED GULL  *Larus ridibundus  (B,W)*
F       1st juv Skinflats 30 Jun (GO). 3600 Blackness 10 Dec (MA).
C       470 Gartmorn 30 Jan (AT).
S       400 prs on Carron Valley Res island 26 May (AKM). 25 prs Flanders Moss in Jun,
        disappeared at end of month (DP). 640 on winter cereal Lecropt 9 Jan. 390
        L.Watston 22 Feb. 560 on pasture Blairlogie 14 Nov & 650 Fallin 16 Dec (CJH
        RD).

COMMON GULL *Larus canus (B,W)*
S     500 Cambusmore GP 10 Aug (PWS). Leucistic bird at Fallin 21 Dec (RD).
LESSER BLACK-BACKED GULL *Larus fuscus (b,S)*
       Few mid-winter records, as usual. Spring arrival probably represented in February by 1 at Larbert on 13th, Cambusmore & Skinflats on 20th, Stirling on 21st (MA PWS DT), in March by 13 Skinflats on 8th & 17 Cambuskenneth on 19th (GO AT).
F     30 Larbert 17 Sep, 2 on 10 & 17 Dec. 1 Skinflats 26 Nov & 3 Dec (MA GO).
C     55 AoT on Menstrie bond roofs 6 May (CJH). 1 Gartmorn 20 Nov (AT).
S     2 Carron Valley Res 15 Jan & 13 Feb, 1 on 19 Nov & 16 Dec (DAC). 185 Buchlyvie 18 Apr (DK). 62 L.Coulter 27 Oct (NB). 1 Cambuskenneth 16 Dec (AT).
HERRING GULL *Larus argentatus (b,S,W)*
C     15 AoT Menstrie bond roofs 6 May. 1500 Blackdevonmouth tip 1 Nov. 6600 Cambus roost flight on 25 Jan (CJH).
S     1800 Fallin tip 8 Aug & 5000 on 21 Dec (CJH RD).
*ICELAND GULL *Larus glaucoides*
S     1 Fallin 28/29 Dec (RD HC).
*GLAUCOUS GULL *Larus hyperboreus*
S     1 ad Fallin 16 & 23 Dec (RD HC).
GREAT BLACK-BACKED GULL *Larus marinus (S,W)*
       Highly under-reported (Ed).
F     51 Kinneil 1 Jan (MA). 108 Higgins Neuk roost flight 2 Jan (CJH). 24 Slamannan 21 Feb (NB).
KITTIWAKE *Rissa tridactyla (P,w)*
F     60 Kinneil 28 Oct (DMB). 1 Blackness 5 Nov (DT).
SANDWICH TERN *Sterna sandvicensis (P)*
F     2 Blackness 1 May, 220 (80 juv) on 23 Jul, 400 on 19 Aug (MA DT), *late arrival (Ed)*. 240 Kinneil & 85 Carriden 10 Sep (DMB).
COMMON TERN *Sterna hirundo (B)*
F     1st, 2 Skinflats 28 Apr (GO). 84 Grangemouth Docks 11 May & 114 pairs on 28th (DMB).
GUILLEMOT *Uria aalge (W)*
F     148 Blackness 30 Jan & 42 on 20 Feb (MA). 15 Kinneil & 15 Carriden 10 Dec (DMB).
C     1 Tullibody Inch 12 Nov (DMB).
S     1 Airthrey 14 & 26 Nov, found dead 7 Dec (MVB AT).
FERAL PIGEON *Columba livia (B,W)*
S     200 Lecropt 12 Nov (CJH).
STOCK DOVE *Columba oenas (B,W)*
       Widespread in small numbers, surely much overlooked. BBS records only in farmland, 1 per 10 km (as 1999).
F     Maxima of 10 Skinflats 1 Jan & 12 on 5 May (GO).
C     10 S.Alloa "bridge" 19 Nov (CJH).
S     35 Lecropt 13 Feb & 45 on 26th (DT DOE)
WOODPIGEON *Columba palumba (B,W)*
       Greatly underreported. BBS shows 52 per 10 km on farmland, 2x more than urban or conifer habitats; no general trend over last 6 years (NB).
F     113 Larbert 14 Jan (AS).
S     300 Blairlogie 11 Dec (CJH).
COLLARED DOVE *Streptopelia decaocto (B,W)*
       Greatly under-reported. Scarce away from suburbs and large farms, BBS frequency as 1999, 22 per 10 Km in suburbs (NB).

S    1-4 Killin 3 Feb to 27 Oct (PWS). 20 Thornhill carse 23 Oct, 15 Cambuskenneth 25 Nov, 17 Hill o' Row 27 Dec & 66 Lecropt on 21 Oct (DJC AT DT).

CUCKOO   *Cuculus canorus (B)*
First records in April at Menteith Hills, Arklet & Camelon 22th, Aberfoyle 29th (SS DT MA KD). BBS shows 3 per 10 Km in conifers/moorland edge, few elsewhere; has fluctuated irregularly since 1994 (NB).
S    5 sites in Trossachs + Flanders Moss (SS DT MA KD DOE).

BARN OWL   *Tyto alba (b,w)*
S    3 nest sites around Doune (KD). Also, through year, 5 sites on Carse of Stirling, 1 Braes of Doune, Callander, Strathyre (SS DAC SZ JW DMB DJC).

TAWNY OWL   *Strix aluco  (B,W)*
Reported Bo'ness, Tilllicoultry, Stirling, Buchlyvie, Braes of Doune, Blackwater marshes, Killin (AS AT CJM DAC DP DJC PWS).

LONG-EARED OWL   *Asio otus (b,w)*
F    Bred Skinflats 2Y on 16 Jun (AB).
C    Juv heard Cambus 15 Jul (CJH).
S    Bred Doune, 2Y in May (KD DOE).

SHORT-EARED OWL   *Asio flammeus (b,W)*
Remains very local, possible breeding only on Gargunnock Hills.
F    1 Skinflats 1-6 Apr, now rare there (GO DT). 1 Kinneil 11 May & 30 Sep. 2 Grangemouth 10 Dec (DMB).
S    2 Earl's Hill 22 Mar & 4 on 4 May (DT). 1 Lossburn Res 19 Feb & 2 on 11 Mar (AT).

SWIFT   *Apus apus (B)*
First records in May: 1 Menteith Hills on 5th, on the 6th at Bonnybridge, BoA, Doune, Strathyre (DT MA DMB CJM DOE DJC). Typical last dates were in Aug – Dunblane on 8th, Stirling 11th, BoA 13th, Flanders Moss 14th, Skinflats 23rd, Lecropt 28th (NB DT CJH DP DMB), but very late birds at Fallin on 30 Sep & Plean CP on 1 Oct (RD).
F    31 Skinflats 8 Jul (GO).
S    35 BoA 24 & 27 Jul, 35 Lecropt 12 Aug (CJH DT).

NIGHTJAR   *Caprimulgus caprimulgus (b?)*
No records this year

KINGFISHER   *Alcedo atthis (b,w)*
Appears to be maintaining good numbers throughout but only 4 records Apr-Jul.
F    Reported on Carron (to Larbert), lower Avon, Kinneil (MA AB GO DMB).
C    Reported R.Devon (Cambus to Tillicoultry), Gartmorn Dam (GEL PD KW DAC AT).
S    4 sites on R.Teith, Blairdrummond-Callander (NB DOE MW KD DP RD). 1 on Allan at BoA Apr-Nov (CJM CJH DT)

WRYNECK   *Jynx torquilla*
F    1 E.Grangemouth 10 Sep (DMB).

GREEN WOODPECKER   *Picus viridis  (B,W)*
Widespread Stirling, Hillfoots;  apparently absent Falkirk.
C    4 sites Menstrie to Harviestoun. 1 Gartmorn 28 Dec (AT AS CJH).
S    Noted L.Ard Forest through summer & 5 sites from Braes of Doune to Blairlogie (DOE CJH IW DAC KD MVB). 1 on edge of Flanders Moss near Thornhill 10 Aug was lst record (SS). 1 Collymoon Moss 15 Aug (DP). 1 Carron Valley Res 13 Oct (GJB).

GREAT SPOTTED WOODPECKER   *Dendrocopus major  (B,W)*
Under-recorded, especially in Stirling. BBS shows 2 per 10 Km in conifers (NB).
F    1 Skinflats Jan/Feb & Aug. 1 Grangemouth 6 Feb, 1 Larbert 27 Aug (AB GO MA).

C    M Harviestoun 1 Jan (AT). 1 Alva Woodland Park 26 Mar (CJH).

S    Reported L.Katrine, L.Voil, L.Ard Forest, Callander, Doune, Airthrey, Stirling (NB DAC CJH DK JW).

SKYLARK *Alauda arvensis (B,W)*

BBS shows 49 on moorland, 10 in conifers, 24 on farmland (marked increase over 1999) and none in 'Urban'.

Singing Braes of Doune 20 Feb & Cambuskenneth on 27th, Skinflats from 1 Mar (KD AT AB).

F    33 Skinflats 17 Jan, 50 ->SE on 25 Sep & 100 in stubble 30 Dec (AB).

C    2 prs Blackdevonmouth 8 May (CJH).

S    10 AoT Flanders Moss 1 May (DOE). 130 Lecropt 13 Feb, 206 on 17 Dec & 240 on 31st. 100 Thornhill 23 Feb & 80 on 19 Nov (MVB CJH SS).

SAND MARTIN *Riparia riparia (B)*

1st records in March: 10 Blairdrummond on 20th, 25 Lake of Menteith on 21st, 2 Thornhill on 25th, 2 Camelon on 26th & 10 Airthrey on 27th. Last 100 Cambusmore 9 Sep & 4 Skinflats on 1 Oct (KD DT SS MA DMB PWS).

S    500 Killin 30 May (PWS). Small colony L.Voil 7 Aug (DP).

SWALLOW *Hirundo rustica (B)*

1st records in April: 1 Buchlyvie on 7th, 1 Blairdrummond & 2 Bo'ness on 8th, Airthrey on 9th, widespread arrival 16-28th. (DAC DOE MA DMB et al). Last in October: Plean CP on 1st, Braes of Doune on 2nd, 6 BoA on 7th; 3 Cambus, 6 Bonnybridge, 8 Camelon & 17 Kennetpans on 8th, 1 Stirling on 14th (AB KD AT CJH MA DT). Largest flock was 35 Skinflats 29 Aug (GO).

HOUSE MARTIN *Delichon urbica (B)*

Late arrival in late April: Airthrey on 20th, Gartmorn on 22nd, Camelon on 23rd, widespread from 27th (DMB DAC MA DOE). Typical late dates were Airthrey 4 Oct & Stirling on 11th (DMB DT), but exceptionally late birds at Stirling on 22 & 28 Nov (IW RJ). BBS this year shows numbers almost halved, 9 per 10 km , back to normal with Swallow three times as common

F    35 Skinflats 29 Aug (AB).

S    20 nest Killin (Br.of Lochay) 21 May (PWS). 50 at colony Braes of Doune 15 May (DOE).

TREE PIPIT *Anthus trivialis (B)*

BBS shows 5 per 10 km in conifers (only 33 % of 98 & 99 figures), very scarce in farmland. Otherwise greatly under-reported.

1st record was a migrant in transit at Lecropt 21 Apr (DT); at Cambusmore and Inversnaid on 28th (DOE).

MEADOW PIPIT *Anthus pratensis (B,W)*

BBS shows 15 per 10 km in moor/conifer edge, 145 on moorland, & 4 on farmland. Overall similar to 98 & 99.

Relatively scarce midwinter: 24 Blairlogie 14 Jan, 28 Blackdevonmouth on 18th & 25 Cambus on 25th (CJH). Spring passage: arrival Killin 100 on 2 Apr, 150 Lanrick on 15th (PWS DT)

S    200 Flanders Moss 28 Aug & 90 Kinbuck 12 Sep (DP MVB).

GREY WAGTAIL *Motacilla cinerea (B,w)*

15 January records, 5 on the Devon, Dollar-Alva, and 8 on Carron below Denny. Scarcer after mid November, 12 in Dec from 9 sites. Widespread records from early Feb to early Mar suggest spring return.

Fair year W.Stirling (HR). Spring/summer records at 9 sites in all areas. Family party on Carron west of Larbert, Juvs can disperse early, 1 at Blackdevonmouth from 17 Jul (MA CJH).

PIED WAGTAIL  Motacilla alba  (B, w)
  BBS shows 5 per 10 Km in Farmland & 7 in "Urban", similar to 1999.
  Noted at only 2 sites in Jan (14 Lecropt on 9th) but 14 in Dec (21 Gart on 12th, 23 Cambuskenneth on 16th & 11 Callander on 18th) (CJH AT NB).
F   White Wagtails M.a.alba : 1 or 2 at Skinflats 4 Apr to 4 May. 1 Kinneil 18 Mar, 24 Apr & 10 Sep (GO DT DMB).
C   White Wagtails M.a.alba : 1 Tullibody Inch 23 Apr & 1 Blackdevonmouth 17 Sep (DMB).
S   100 Killin 2 Apr (PWS). 87 BoA 7 Oct (AT).

WAXWING  Bombycilla garrulus
S   Influx in late Dec: First 5 at Stirling 27 Dec, fed on apples to 30th; 25 at Business Park 30th & 31st (IW DK AB). 4 Lecropt on 30th & 1 BoA on 31st (MVB AT).

DIPPER  Cinclus cinclus  (B,W)
  Widespread song in Jan.
F   8 on R.Carron, Carron-Bonnybridge 16 Jan (MA).
C   28 on Devon, Alva-Dollar, in Jan (only 8 on 14 Mar); 17 in Nov; also at rivermouth (Cambus) Jan & Oct/Nov (DE GEL DAC). 1 Blackdevonmouth 6 Nov (AT).
S   Fair year W.Stirling (HR).

WREN  Troglodytes troglodytes  (B,W)
  Under-recorded (Ed). BBS shows 71 per 10 Km in conifers, 25 on farmland, 22 in 'Urban' & 1 on moorland. Highest overall total since 1996, up 35% over 1999, mainly in conifers.

HEDGE SPARROW  Accentor modularis  (B,W)
  Under-recorded (Ed). BBS shows 11 per 10 Km in 'Urban', 6 in conifers & 9 in farmland. Overall figures close to 7 year average.

ROBIN  Erithacus rubecula  (B,W)
  Under-recorded (Ed). BBS shows 43 per 10 km in conifers, 16 on farmland & 10 in 'Urban'. Overall figures up 13 % over 1999, but close to 7 year average.
  1st autumn song at Airthrey 5 Aug; singing after dark in Stirling 14 Nov (CJH AT).

REDSTART  Phoenicurus phoenicurus  (B)
  1st of spring, singing at Lake of Menteith 7 May (RAB).
S   38 prs Trossachs colony (36 in 1999), reared 105 Y – later broods affected by predation by Great Spotted Woodpeckers (HR). Pr with 2Y Braes of Doune 9 Jul (KD). 13 Y fledged from 2 boxes at G.Finglas scheme (DJC).

WHINCHAT  Saxicola rubetra  (B)
  BBS shows 1 per 10 Km on moorland, half the 1999 frequency & a quarter the seven year average.
  1st of spring 1 Thornhill 22 Apr & 3 Kinneil on 30th; Skinflats on 7 May, Flanders Moss on 12th & Invertrossachs on 13th (SS DT AB DOE).
S   Pr + 5Y Killin 8 Jul (PWS).

STONECHAT  Saxicola torquata  (b,w)
  BBS shows 1 per 10 Km on moorland & no other records. Overall close to 7 year average.
F   M Skinflats 8 Oct to 3 Nov & F on 17 Dec (GO). M Kinneil 1 Oct (DT).
C   2 Alloa Inches (Rhind) 28 Dec (AT).
S   In breeding season noted at Earl's Hill, L.Arklet,Thornhill, Flanders Moss (pr+3Y), Doune (pr+3Y), G.Ogle (4 prs) (DT SS DP DOE). In winter/autumn at 9 further sites, mainly Trossachs and northern hills but also Carron Valley Res, Kippen Muir, Buchlyvie, Sheriffmuir. (DAC NB GO AB DMB).

WHEATEAR *Oenanthe oenanthe (B)*
    BBS shows 3 per 10 km, only on moorland; half the frequency over 1997-99 but similar to 1994/95.
    First dates on breeding grounds were Tillicoultry Glen 25 Mar & Balquhidder on 31st, G.Buckie 15 Apr (AT KD DT). 1 Kinneil 9 Apr, widespread after 24th; on estuary to 7 May. Autumn migrants on estuary mainly early Sep, late birds at Cambus (Greenland form) on 28 Sep & Kinneil on 30th (AT KD DT GO DMB).
*RING OUZEL *Turdus torquatus (b)*
S    1st of spring in Balquhidder, Creag McRannach 31 Mar (3 on 24 Apr) & Monachyle Glen on 9 Apr (KD DJC). M Ben Lui summit 29 Jun & 20 Jul (KD).
C    F Alva Glen 23 Apr (DK).
BLACKBIRD *Turdus merula (B,W)*
    BBS shows 116 per 10 km in 'Urban' & 29 on farmland. Overall close to 1998 & 99 & the 7 year average.
F    11 Wallacebank Wood 15 Jan (AS).
S    10 Dunblane 3 Aug & Killin 23 Oct (NB PWS).
FIELDFARE *Turdus pilaris (W)*
    Spring departure meagre, last flocks Doune 18 Apr, but 13 Blackdevonmouth 15 May (KD AT).
    Autumn arrival late, only Oct records were at Killin, small flocks on 23rd & many flocks on 24th. 160 Blackdevonmouth 1 Nov, 120 ->W Airthrey on 9th, 2000 Lecropt on 11th. (PWS CJH MVB DT).
F    161 Skinflats 13 Nov was only large flock (GO).
S    108 Blairlogie on 16 Feb & 150 Braes of Doune on 20th (CJH MVB). Only large Dec flock was 225 Braes of Doune on 5th (NB).
SONG THRUSH *Turdus philomelos (B,W)*
    BBS shows 14 per 10 km in 'Urban', 10 in farmland & 10 in conifers. Overall frequency highest since 1996 but close to 7 year average.
    Few in January – 1 Airthrey, 1 Skinflats, 2 Doune. 8 L.Katrine 28 Feb represents spring arrival, but not noted Killin till 28 Mar. 7 sites, Buchlyvie to Larbert & Killin, in Dec (CJH GO AT NB PWS DAC MA).
F    4 Fallin 1 Oct considered migrants (RD).
REDWING *Turdus iliacus (W)*
    1st of autumn 7 Camelon 8 Oct; 100 Kippen Muir on 21st, large night passage on 22nd at Doune, many flocks Killin on 23rd & 24th, 500 ->W Airthrey & 2500 ->NW BoA on 24th. Max later were 300 Blackdevonmouth 1 Nov & 106 Larbert on 17 Dec (MA DT DOE PWS MVB CJH).
MISTLE THRUSH *Turdus viscivorus (B,W)*
    BBS shows 2 per 10 km in conifers & 1 on farmland, as 1999. Overall close to the 7 year average.
    30 Braes of Doune 30 Jun, 25 Airthrey 25 Aug; otherwise only 6 sites in autumn (DT DMB et al).
GRASSHOPPER WARBLER *Locustella naevia (b)*
F    Singing at Skinflats from 22 Apr to 2 Jun (GO AB MA DT).
C    1 Cambus 15 Jul (CJH)
S    2 Flanders Moss 1 May & 1 on 9 Jun. 1 Carron Valley Res 2 Jul & 1 Cowie on 19th (DOE DP DAC DT) .
SEDGE WARBLER *Acrocephalus schoenobaenus (B)*
    BBS shows highest total in 7 years, twice the average.
    1st record Skinflats 24 Apr, Camelon 27th, Kinneil & Blairdrummond 30th; widespread by 7 May. Last were 1 Skinflats 29 Aug and Kinneil 10 Sep. (GO MA DT DOE et al).

C    15 AoT Blackdevonmouth 11 May (DOE).
WHITETHROAT *Sylvia communis (B)*
BBS shows highest total in 7 years, three times the average.
1st records in April: 24th Skinflats, Camelon 27th, Cambus, Carronshore &
Kinneil 30th; May 2nd Lecropt, widespread by 7th (GO MA ATAB DT DOE et
al).
GARDEN WARBLER *Sylvia borin (B)*
Very scarce in BBS surveys, on average 25 % as frequent as Blackcap.
1st records in May: Camelon on 1st, Port of Menteith on 3rd, Braes of Doune on
4th (MA DOE KD). Last at Skinflats 28 Aug, eating berries (AB)
BLACKCAP *Sylvia atricapilla (B)*
BBS shows increase of 30 % compared with 1999. Overall close to 7 year
average, but only 1.5 per 10 Km in two best habitats.
Winter records: Stirling, 2M from 9 Jan to 8 Apr (CJM), F on 12 Dec & M from
14th to year end (JGH) - at bird tables, aggressive to other species; M on 30 Nov
& 3 (2F) on 28 Dec, fed on apples (IW). 1Carronshore 16 to 23 Dec (AB). Birds at
Stirling 19 Mar & BoA 9 Apr possibly overwintered, spring arrivals were later in
Apr – 5 Polmont on 21st, Gartmorn on 22nd, 2 Skinflats on 23rd (RJ DMB MA
DAC). Last Kinneil 30 Sep (DMB).
WOOD WARBLER *Phylloscopus sibilatrix (B)*
Underrecorded
1st records Lake of Menteith 30 Apr, Callander on 2 May & Invertrossachs on
7th (DOE MA RAB). Low numbers in Trossachs oakwood (HR).
CHIFFCHAFF *Phylloscopus collybita (B)*
1st records in March: Plean on 19th, Doune Ponds & Blairlogie 25th, Alva,
Larbert, Polmont (4) & Skinflats 26th. 1 Buchlyvie 1 Oct, 1 Airthrey on 4 Oct &
5 Dec (DT DOE DAC CJH MA GO DMB).
WILLOW WARBLER *Phylloscopus trochilus (B)*
BBS shows 56 per 10 km in conifers, 17 in farmland, 22 in 'Urban'; 6 % up on
1998 (NB).
1st records in April: Airthrey on 6th, Larbert & Plean on 14th, Skinflats on 16th,
Thornhill on 18th & Carronshore on 19th; widespread by 23rd (DMB MA DT
GO SS AB et al).
S    Juvs in garden at Stirling from 23 Jul, last on 16 Sep (RJ).
GOLDCREST *Regulus regulus (B,W)*
BBS shows 21 per 10 km in conifers, 1 in farmland & 'Urban'. Overall up 88 %
over 1999, now close to 7 year average.
Widespread in small numbers, max 6 Wallacebank Wood (Falkirk) 14 Feb (AS).
F    Through year at Skinflats (AB).
SPOTTED FLYCATCHER *Muscicapa striata (B)*
Under-recorded (Ed). Scarce in BBS, 1 per 10 km, only in farmland; slight
increase this year, slightly above 7 year average (NB).
1st records: Doune & BoA 12 May, L. Katrine on 21st, Tamfourhill on 28th,
S.L.Tay on 8 Jun (DOE DMB DAC MA PWS).
S    3 AoT Lendrick 13 Jun. Many seen Stronachlachar-Glengyle 16 Jul. Family
parties at Doune, Flanders Moss (DJC KD DOE).
PIED FLYCATCHER *Ficedula hypoleuca (b)*
S    Numbers at Trossachs colony 47 % down, 27 prs reared 70 Y – poor success,
much predation by Great Spotted Woodpeckers (HR). 11 prs (7 successful) at
G.Finglas boxes reared 31Y (DJC).
LONG-TAILED TIT *Aegithalos caudatus (B,W)*
Always the scarcest of the four tits, BBS shows similar to 1999, well below 7 year

average.
F   6 Bo'ness 21 Feb, 14 Skinflats 1 Nov & 6 Kinneil 26 Dec. 15 at Carronshore 13 Feb
    & 19 Nov (AS GO AB). Pr + 7Y Camelon 28 May (MA).
C   10 Harviestoun 1 Jan & 12 Alva 25 Dec (AT).
S   10 Fallin 5 Oct (RD). 14 Stirling 18 Nov (IW). 10+9 Lecropt 16 Nov & 10 on 16
    Dec (CJH DT).
COAL TIT *Parus ater (B,W)*
    Greatly under-recorded (Ed). BBS shows 25 records per 10 km in conifers, 4 on
    farmland. 53 % increase over 1999, reversing 6 year decline but still 28 % less
    than average (NB).
BLUE TIT *Parus caeruleus (B,W)*
    Under-recorded (Ed). BBS shows 27 per 10 Km in 'urban' squares, 18 on
    farmland & 5 in conifers. Overall 27 % decrease over 1999 but close to average
    (NB).
S   10 prs (8 successful) at G.Finglas boxes reared 47 Y (DJC). 5 prs at Trossachs
    scheme (15 in 1999, HR). 44 Dunblane 12 Oct & 10 Stirling 12 Oct (NB JW)
GREAT TIT *Parus major (B,W)*
    Under-recorded (Ed). BBS shows 4 per 10 km in 'Urban' squares, 8 on farmland
    and 1in conifers – big drop in urban and overall 15% drop since 1999.
S   8 prs at G.Finglas boxes reared 35 Y (DJC). 19 prs at Trossachs scheme (29 in
    1999, HR).
TREECREEPER *Certhia familiaris (B,W)*
    Under-recorded (Ed). BBS shows 1.4 per 10 km on farmland, possibly small
    decrease over 1999 but close to average.
F   5 Wallacebank Wood 14 Jan (AS).
JAY *Garrulus glandarius (B,W)*
    Very scarce in BBS records, fairly steady decline since 1995 but samples small.
F   All year at Torwood – Wallacebank Wood (AB AS) – continuous with range
    around Stirling (Ed). 5 Bonnybridge 17 Dec (MA).
C   3 Gartmorn 1 Jan, near Alva Apr & Dec (AT).
S   Recorded from Cardross and Aberfoyle to Callander and BoA, north to L.Voil
    & Killin and also Carron Valley (DAC NB AT).
MAGPIE *Pica pica (B,W)*
    Its abundance around Stirling is not necessarily noted in the west and east of
    the area (Ed). BBS shows 25 per 10 km in 'urban' squares & 7 in farmland.
    Numbers stable since 1997, were higher in previous 3 years.
F   5 Bo'ness 12 Mar (AS).
C   14 Cambus Pools 26 Mar (AT).
S   13 Stirling 22 Feb & 18 Fallin 11 Oct (NB JW). 81 at Airthrey roost 18 Dec & 36
    on 27th (AT). 4 Braes of Doune (E.Lundy, sole record) 13 Oct (KD).
JACKDAW *Corvus monedula (B,W)*
    An overlooked species, about 3 reports (Ed). BBS shows highest frequency (34
    per 10 km$^{-1}$) in farmland, 9 in urban areas, numbers stable over last 5 years. *Nb
    BBS data misquoted in 1999 report, farmland overlooked, Ed.*
    400 Sheardale 1 Jan (AT).
S   350 BoA p.m roost flight 23 Jun, 480 at Airthrey roost (with Magpies) 18 Dec
    (CJH AT).
ROOK *Corvus frugilegus (B,W)*
    BBS suggest numbers down 50 % on 1999 (similar and erratic fluctuations in
    previous years). Rookery counts: BoA(N) 90 in pines; BoA(S) 155; Witches Craig
    53, Myretoun 47; 45 Menstrie nursery (new in 1996). Total 337 (517 in 1999,
    decrease of 35 %). (CJH).

S   46 nests Kincardine in Menteith. 500 Blairlogie 16 Feb, 1000 Throsk 9 Nov (CJH RD).

CARRION CROW   *Corvus corone (B,W)*
Possibly the most widespread species of all: BBS shows 39 per 10 km in 'Urban' squares, 52 in farmland, 8 in conifer & 52 on moorland. Apparently large switches in preferences among habitats this year, but overall rise since 1996.

S   34 Braes of Doune 20 Feb (MVB). Hoodies: 6 sites in the usual breeding range L.Katrine-G.Lochay, usually less than 5 but 50 G.Lochay 19 Feb (NB DAC DT). 1 hybrid Lecropt 24 Jan (CJH).

RAVEN   *Corvus corax (B,W)*
S   17 territories checked, 14 pairs. 12 successful pairs of which 7 raised 21 Y (PSA). Collecting nest material G.Lochay 26 Feb (RAB). 12 G.Casaig 8 Aug (DJC). Outwith of main breeding areas: Max 3 Thornhill Feb/Mar, Jul – Sep (SS DP). 1 Airthrey 22 Feb & 18 Aug (DMB). 3 Lecropt 9 Sep (DT).

STARLING   *Sturnus vulgaris (B,W)*
Greatly under-reported (Ed). BBS shows most frequent in 'Urban' squares. Overall 55% increase over 1999 – but possibly observability varies between years with fledging date.

F   543 Denny 9 Jan. 600 on wet pasture Slamannan 27 Oct (NB). 1300 at Kincardine Bridge roost 18 Oct, 4000 on 21 Nov but half left downriver (CJH).

S   220 Stirling roost 7 Mar. 700 at pre-roost Forthbank 17 Oct (AT).

HOUSE SPARROW   *Passer domesticus (B,W)*
Under-recorded (Ed). BBS shows 78 per 10 km in 'Urban' areas, 28 on farmland. Overall increased 70 % on 1999 data, back to 1994-96 level.

S   31 Blairlogie 14 Jan (CJH). 56 Dunblane 21 Mar (NB). Surveys on Thornhill Carse showed 105 on 23 Oct & 120 on 9 Dec (DJC).

TREE SPARROW   *Passer montanus (B,W)*
Scarce on BBS transects, only on farmland. Overall back close to seven year average. Widely reported in small numbers from Thornhill eastwards.

F   14 Bonnybridge 12 Mar (MA). 9 Kinneil 17 Jan & 10 Sep, 15 Skinflats 3 Dec (DT GO).

C   In breeding season at Gartmorn, Rhynd (Alloa) & Blackdevonmouth (DAC DMB). 20 Inch of Ferryton 10 Dec (CJH).

S   30 Lecropt 19 Sep & 33 on 16 Nov (DT CJH). 20 Drip Carse 27 Feb & 30 on 27 Nov (DAC IW). 27 Thornhill Carse 24 Nov & 34 on 9 Dec (DJC CJM DOE).

CHAFFINCH   *Fringilla coelebs (B,W)*
BBS shows 94 per 10 km in conifers, 52 on farmland & 20 in 'Urban' squares, overall slightly less than 7 year mean.

S   600 Kippenrait 16 Jan. 550 Kinbuck 25 Mar & 300 on 30 Dec. 450 Lecropt on 20 Feb & 350 on 31 Dec (MVB).

BRAMBLING   *Fringilla montifringilla (W)*
Several moderate spring flocks, very scarce in autumn.

F   Late bird, M Skinflats 7 Apr (AB).
50 Kippenrait 16 Jan. 20 Lecropt 20 Feb & 50 on 12 Mar (MVB). 1 Fallin 1 Oct & 3 on 6th (RD). 4 Mine Wood (BoA) 31 Dec (AT).

GREENFINCH   *Carduelis chloris (B,W)*
Underrecorded. BBS shows 46 per 10 km in 'Urban' squares & 10 in farmland. Overall as 1999 & close to 7 year mean.

F   80 Skinflats 23 Aug (DT).

S   150 Lecropt 4 Jan & 100 on 12 Aug (MVB DT). 67 Dunblane garden 18 Jan (NB). 16 Strathyre garden 28 Dec was highest count out of lowlands (DJC).

GOLDFINCH  *Carduelis carduelis (B,W)*

      BBS shows 3 per 10 km in farmland and 1 in 'Urban" squares, 37 % over 1999.

F     54 Skinflats 5 Feb, still 18 on 14 Apr; 28 on 3 Nov (GO). 65 Carron Works 17 Sep (MA).

C     17 Blackdevonmouth 3 Sep. 11 Alva 11 Oct (CJH AT).

S     300 Kinbuck 26 Jan & 150 on 10 Mar; 70 on 22 Dec. 100 Kippenrait 16 Jan. 80 Lecropt 12 Mar (NB MVB). 31 Stirling 5 Feb (AT). 16 on thistles G.Finglas 11 Oct – highest count in hills (DJC).

SISKIN  *Carduelis spinus (B,W)*

      BBS shows 3 per 10 km  in conifers, 1 on farmland. Overall lowest since 1996. In gardens at Bo'ness & Stirling, especially Mar & Apr (AS RJ).

F     35 Skinflats 20 Apr (GO). 38 Little Denny Res 12 Sep (NB).

S     35 L.Lubnaig 18 Jan & 45 on 27 Nov. 25 Callander 18 Dec (NB). 30 BoA 4 Oct (CJH). 100 Strathyre 26 Oct (DJC).

LINNET  *Carduelis cannabina (B,W)*

      BBS shows 2 per 10 km on moorland, 4 on farmland, 4 in 'Urban' & 2 in conifers. Stable over last 5 years.

F     400 Kinneil 6 Feb & 250 on 1 Oct (DT). 400 Skinflats 30 Nov (AB).

C     100 Glenochil 15 Jan & 60 on 24 Nov. 30 Alva 1 Oct (AT IW).

S     800 Kippenrait 16 Jan. 92 Kinbuck 26 Jan; 530 17 Sep & 550 on 8 Oct. 500 Lecropt 28 Oct & 350 on 16 Dec (MVB NB DT). 120 Lanrick 20 Feb, 200 Hill of Row 21 Oct. 40 Flanders Moss 1 May (DOE).

TWITE  *Carduelis flavirostris (b,W)*

F     13 Skinflats 5 Nov, on saltmarsh. 25 Kinneil 23 Jan (AB).

S     Spring/summer reports from G.Finglas (3 sites), Braes of Doune (Severie). 80 Finglas Res 13 Sep (DJC DOE). 6 in plantation Sheriffmuir 19 Feb (AT). 500 Kinbuck 12 Nov & 300 on 16 Dec (MVB).

REDPOLL  *Carduelis cabaret (b,W)*

      BBS shows 6 per 10 Km in conifers, overall only one half of 6 year mean.

F     3 Kinneil 8 Jan (AB). *sole record (Ed).*

C     5 Blackdevonmouth 5 Dec (DMB).

S     50 G.Dochart 26 Jan, fed on birch & heather seeds (PWS). In Apr/May small numbers at L.Katrine, Menteith Hills, Balquhidder (DT). 38 Carron Valley Res 30 Oct (AKM). 15 Fallin 27 Dec (RD).

COMMON CROSSBILL  *Loxia curvirostra (b,W)*

      BBS shows 2 per 10 km in conifers, a fall to 25 % of 6 year mean.

S     In L.Ard Forest May to Jul, 10 on 24 Sep (with juvs being fed); 24 in larches 4 Nov (DOE CJH DAC JNW). 9 Invertrossachs 1 Jul; 12 Braes of Doune 4 Nov & at L.Mahaick on 7th (DOE DJC). 7 Carron Valley Res 15 Oct (GO), present to 16 Dec, when 8 (2 juv being fed, DAC).

BULLFINCH  *Pyrrhula pyrrhula (B,W)*

      BBS shows 1 per 10 km in conifers, further drop & now overall lowest figure for 7 years & only one-seventh of mean.

C     7 Gartmorn 1 Nov & 5 on 20th (AS AT).

S     20 L.Venachar 14 Jan (DJC). Fed on heather seeds Balquhidder (2 Km from trees) 24 Mar. 6 Braes of Doune 15 Sep (KD).

SNOW BUNTING  *Plectrophenax nivalis (W)*

S     In Feb, 8 in Dochart hills on 13th & 30 Upper G.Lochay on 19th (RAB DT).

YELLOWHAMMER  *Emberiza citrinella (B,W)*

      BBS shows 12 per 10 km on farmland, now back close to 6 year mean after 3 poor years.

F     23 Airth 10 Feb (GO). 12 Skinflats 5 Nov (AB).

48   *C.J. Henty*

C    11 Tillicoultry 23 Dec (AT).
S    4 AoT Flanders Moss 12 May (DOE). 58 Cambuskenneth 5 Feb (AT). 50 Thornhill 4 Mar. (DAC). 95 Lecropt 1 Jan & 85 on 31 Dec (MVB).
REED BUNTING  *Emberiza schoeniclus (B,W)*
     BBS shows 2 per 10 km in farmland & 2 on Moorland, overall at 6 year mean and no trend.
F    15 Skinflats 13 Jan (GO).
C    2 AoT Cambus Pools 7 May (CJH). 6 AoT Blackdevonmouth 11 May (DOE).
S    2 AoT Flanders Moss (DP). Pr + 2Y Killin 8 Jul (PWS). 28 Lecropt 16 Jan & 67 on 20 Feb (MVB). 55 by Thornhill 20 Feb & 24 on 4 Mar (SS DAC).
*CORN BUNTING  *Emberiza calandra*
     1 Skinflats 26 Nov (DMB).


## ESCAPED SPECIES

SNOW GOOSE  *Anser*
S    1 white phase with Canada Geese at Blairdrummond 17 Mar (KD).
RED-LEGGED PARTRIDGE  *Alectoris rufa*
S    65 Cromlix/Cambushinnie 22 Jan, scarcer in autumn, possibly fewer released (MVB).
EAGLE / HORNED OWL  *Bubo bubo/virginianus*
S    1 Braes of Doune Sep-Nov (KD W.Howlett). Local press reports from Stirling in the autumn claimed that a bird was terrorising dog walkers in a public park.. A ringed bird at Blairdrummond Jan-Apr laid an egg (DOE KD). This individual was positively identifed as the palaearctic species *Bubo bubo*, however the American *B.virginianus* is also widely kept in captivity and no doubt also escapes occasionally; the two species are easily confused and the Horned Owl is not mentioned, let alone described, in european field guides. Thus the editor is not convinced that many "eagle" owls that are reported can be reliably assumed to be the european species, though this is the usual presumption.

# SOME SPIDERS OF FLANDERS MOSS

## J.A. Stewart

The spiders of the Scottish Wildlife Trust's reserve at Flanders Moss (NS635973) have been investigated several times during the last ten years in connection with the Spider Recording Scheme of the British Arachnological Society. The reserve covers part of what remains of a once much more extensive, but still the largest remaining, lowland raised bog in Britain. It lies adjacent to the larger National Nature Reserve and conditions within it are very similar to those described by Nelson (1983/84) in his paper on insects collected from the moss, *i.e.* hummocks and pools with wet heath heathers, sedges, and *Sphagnum* species. The main collecting effort was in 1995 when a series of pitfall traps were run, but hand sampling by sweepnet, sieve and beating was used on occasions before and after that date.

## Results

In all, 118 spider species are recorded, and six species of harvestmen. Most are common and widely distributed and about 20 % of the species are normally restricted to damp habitats.

The most notable find was the jumping spider *Heliophanus dampfi* Schenkel. The previously known distribution of this species was 'widespread in Northern Europe' but up until this find the first and only record of the species in Britain was a female taken in 1989 at Cors Fochno, Dyfi NNR, Cardigan (Williams, 1991). In August 1991 females were swept from Bog Myrtle and Birch saplings at Flanders Moss and in June 1992 male specimens were found. Subsequent sampling has shown that there exists a healthy population of this species within the reserve. Adult females have been noted from April through to September, adult males in June and July only. It is interesting to record that, also in June 1992, the presence of *H. dampfi* was confirmed at Ochtertyre Moss SSSI, just 10 km to the east (D Horsfield, pers. comm.). In early 1996 I was given a collection of unidentified spiders from Nelson's 1981 work (see above). That collection contained a single male specimen of *H. dampfi*.

With over 320 spider species recorded, Perthshire stands at the top of the league of Scotland's counties and nowadays additions to the list come slowly. So it was particularly gratifying to add five new species to the total, all taken by hand sampling, They were *Theridion bimaculatum*, *T. simile*, *Hypsosinga albovittata*, *H. pygmaea* and *Baryphyma pratense*, the latter four being uncommon species in Scotland.

The Lycosids, or wolf spiders, being ground runners, were as usual the most commonly trapped genus and made up 41 % of the overall catch. A surprising feature was the preponderance of *Pirata uliginosus* (177 specimens) over *P. piraticus* (two specimens) as the latter is normally considered to be the more common of the two in wet, marshy places. However, by way of numbers trapped the most common species was the Tetragnathid *Pachygnatha degeeri* with 440 specimens, most of which were taken in the drier area at the edge of the moss, in heather and tufts of grass.

A full species list is given in the Appendix.

**Acknowledgements**

My thanks go to June Waley, Reserve Warden, and the Callander Support Group of the SWT for arranging access to the reserve, to Peter Merrett for the initial identification of *Heliophanus dampfi*, to Bob Saville for identification of the harvestmen, to Richard Bacon for help with the field work, to Isobel Baldwin for field work and help with the preparation of this paper, and to Tim Benton for suggesting improvements to the original draft.

**References**

Nelson, J.M. (1983/4). Some insects from a portion of East Flanders Moss, Central Region. *Forth Naturalist and Historian* 8, 55-63.
Williams, S.A. (1991). *Heliophanus dampfi* Schenkel (Salticidae) in mid-Wales and new to Britain. *Newsl. Br. arachnol. Soc.* 61, 3-4.

APPENDIX – LIST OF SPECIES
(p = trapped in pitfalls, h = collected by hand)

Order ARANEAE (Spiders)

Family DICTYNIDAE – small brownish spiders, makers of mesh type webs.
*Dictyna arundinacea* (h) – very common on heather and other plants where it often spins its web on dry dead heads.

Family GNAPHOSIDAE – mostly nocturnal hunters that spend the day in silken cells under stones and other detritus. They prefer dry sites which they apparently find quite readily in wet, marshy areas.
*Drassodes cupreus* (p,h) – up to 15 mm long, and uniformly fawn in colour, this fierce hunter is commonly found in grass clumps and under stones.
*Haplodrassus signifer* (p,h) – a common species found in similar habitats to the previous one.
*Zelotes latreillei* (p) – a shiny black spider with a widespread distribution in England but recorded in only a few Scottish vice-counties.
*Micaria pulicaria* (p,h) – common and widely distributed, this spider does not limit its search for prey to night time, but can be found running about in bright sunshine. Rather ant-like in appearance with an iridescent abdomen.

Family CLUBIONIDAE – like the previous family the Clubionids are mainly nocturnal hunters that hide during the day in silken cells in a variety of situations.
*Clubiona reclusa* (h) – a common species in low vegetation in damp or marshy sites. The female with egg sac is usually found in a curled leaf.

*C terrestris* (h) – yellowish in colour, this spider can be found on bushes and trees as well as among vegetation and under stones.

*C lutescens* (h) – this species also is found on bushes and trees as well as low vegetation, but usually in damp habitats.

*C trivialis* (h) – common on low vegetation in drier areas.

*C diversa* (p) – common in bog mosses in Scotland but reportedly favours dry sites in southern England.

*Cheiracanthium erraticum* (h) – this species, which is found in heather and grasses, appears to be absent from southern Scotland and northern England. The abdomen has a noticeable red median stripe flanked by yellow stripes.

Family LIOCRANIDAE – another family of nocturnal hunters found mainly in low vegetation and mosses.

*Agroeca proxima* (p) – widely distributed and common on fairly dry heathland.

*Scotina gracilipes* (p) – again resident on dry heaths but less common and locally distributed.

Family ZORIDAE – daytime hunters on the ground and in low vegetation.

*Zora spinimana* (p) – found in detritus, moss and grass in damp places. The female fixes her flat, white egg sac to a stone or a leaf.

Family THOMISIDAE – the so-called 'crab spiders' due to their similarity in shape to small crabs. The first two pairs of legs are longer and stronger than the rest, and the spider can walk sideways and even backwards, albeit usually quite slowly.

*Xysticus cristatus* (p) – by far the most common member of the genus. Found in a wide variety of habitat, from shrub layer to ground level.

*X erraticus* (p) – much less common than *X. cristatus* and almost always found at ground level in grass or under stones etc.

*X ulmi* (h) – locally distributed and uncommon in Scotland. More or less restricted to wet, marshy places.

*Ozyptila trux* (p) – another very common species found in a variety of situations.

Family PHILODROMIDAE – another family of crab-like spiders which was only recently split off from the Thomisidae.

*Philodromus aureolus* (h) – this species, and the next, are equally common and are found on low vegetation, bushes and trees.

*P cespitum* (h)

Family SALTICIDAE – the 'jumping spiders'. With well developed, forward facing eyes the Salticids stalk their prey by sight, then pounce. They are easily seen in hot, sunny weather and perhaps the most often noticed is the black and white 'zebra' spider on house and garden walls.

*Heliophanus dampfi* (p,h) – the first recognised find of this species in Scotland was in August 1991 at Flanders Moss, shortly followed thereafter by specimens at the nearby Ochtertyre Moss (see results above). These remain the only known sites for the species in Scotland. It is given Red Data Book status RDB K *i.e.* insufficiently known, due to its recent discovery.

*Neon reticulatus* (p,h) – occurs commonly in moss in wet, boggy places.

Family LYCOSIDAE – they get the designation 'wolf spiders' from their generally brown colour and their habit of running about at ground level, using well developed eyesight to find prey items. On bright days they may be seen in quantity, the females carrying egg sacs attached to their spinners at the rear of the abdomen.

*Pardosa pullata* (p,h) – a very common species which frequents various habitats including wet places.

*P nigriceps* (p,h) – also common, but often found above ground on vegetation, heather and low bushes.

*Alopecosa pulverulenta* (p,h) – at 10 mm body length much larger than the 6mm *Pardosa* species. Commonly found on open ground and moorland.

*Trochosa terricola* (p) – even larger at up to 14 mm. Common in various, usually damp habitats.

*Pirata piraticus* (p) – the commonest wolf spider of wet, marshy areas with sphagnum moss, and sometimes found running on water.

*P uliginosus* (p,h) – generally much less common than *P.piraticus* but see results above. It normally prefers drier habitats.

Family AGELENIDAE – most spiders in this family are fairly large builders of sheet webs with tubular retreats.

*Cryphoeca silvicola* (h) – at 2-3mm the smallest of the Agelinids. Common in a wide variety of habitats from sea level to mountain tops.

Family HAHNIIDAE – small spiders that spin small sheet webs under stones and in mosses etc. They have spinners arranged in a transverse row as opposed to the cluster formation of other families.

*Antistea elegans* (p,h) – always found in wet places where it makes a web on moss and other low vegetation.

*Hahnia montana* (p,h) – usually found in leaf litter and detritus in woods, but also in low vegetation away from woods.

Family THERIDIIDAE – small to medium sized spiders that make three dimensional webs.

*Episinus angulatus* (h) – not very common. A truncated abdomen makes this genus fairly easy to identify.

*Steatoda phalerata* (p) – local and uncommon. This species is found in dry habitats and normally preys on ants.

*Theridion sisyphium* (h) – the commonest species of the genus. Makes its webs on bushes and low vegetation.

*T impressum* (h) – less common than the previous species but found in similar habitats.

*T simile* (h) – a first record for Perthshire and known in only one other Scottish vice-county. A small (2mm) spider found in heather and other low plants.

*T bimaculatum* (h) – another first record for Perthshire. Widespread but locally distributed and found in low vegetation and bushes.

*T pallens* (h) – a small (1.5-2 mm) spider found very commonly on trees, bushes and other vegetation.

*Enoplognatha ovata* (h) - very commonly found on bushes and other vegetation in a variety of habitats including gardens. Has a yellowish abdomen sometimes furnished with carmine stripes.

*Robertus lividus* (p,h) – common at ground level in a range of habitats including grass and moss.

*Pholcomma gibbum* (p,h) – only 1.5 mm long but common in grass, moss and detritus.

*Theonoe minutissima* (p,h) – as the specific epithet suggests, this species is only 1.5 mm long. Although widely distributed it is not easily found in its preferred habitat at ground level in moss, grass etc.

Family TETRAGNATHIDAE – medium sized spiders with long legs and well developed chelicerae.

*Tetragnatha extensa* (h) – an orb web weaver with an elongate shape which makes it difficult to see when stretched out along a grass stem. Its abdomen has a metallic sheen. Common on vegetation near water and in wet places.

*T montana* (h) – similar to the previous species but often found on trees and bushes.

*Pachygnatha clercki* (h) – less elongate than *Tetragnatha* and makes no web. Hunts at ground level in moss and low vegetation in damp places.

*P degeeri* (p,h) – the commonest species of the genus (see results above) and appears to prefer drier situations.

Family METIDAE – orb web weavers which some consider intermediate between the Tetragnathidae and the Araneidae.

*Metellina segmentata* (h) – an abundant species found wherever there is vegetation that will support its web.

*M mengei* (h) – just as common as the previous species in similar habitats.

*Zygiella atrica* (h) – found on bushes, heather and other vegetation. The characteristc web of this genus has an open sector free of spirals and with a signal line running from the centre of the web to a retreat.

Family ARANEIDAE – all spin orb webs, some of which are very large, and most species have patterned or well marked abdomens.

*Araneus diadematus* (h) – the well known 'garden cross' spider widely distributed in a variety of habitats including gardens.

*A quadratus* (h) – gravid females of this species can be up to 20 mm long. Large webs on bushes, heather and long grasses.

*Larinioides cornutus* (h) – usually found near water with webs strung between reeds or other tall vegetation.

*Nuctenea umbratica* (h) – a dark coloured spider with a flattened abdomen. This modification allows it to hide in narrow crevices.

*Araniella cucurbitina* (h) – recognisable by its green abdomen, and found on trees, bushes and low vegetation.

*Hypsosinga albovittata* (h) – a first record for Perthshire, the only other county records in Scotland being from Angus and Fife. Spins a web low down in heather and other vegetation

*H pygmaea* (h) – another first record for Perthshire, and again few other Scottish records. Webs low down in damp places.

Family LINYPHIIDAE – in Scotland this family accounts for over 50 % of the total species list. Many of these liniphiid species are small and dark coloured, are often referred to as 'money spiders' and are probably most noticeable when dispersing as aeronauts. Those below without comment can be considered as common in a variety of habitats.

*Ceratinella brevipes* (p,h)

*C brevis* (p,h) – less common than *C brevipes*.

*Walckenaeria acuminata* (p,h) – most of the males in this genus have the head modified into lobes or projections.

*W antica* (p,h) – frequent

*W nodosa* (h) – uncommon and usually found in wet places.

*W atrotibialis* (p,h) – uncommon

*W nudipalpis* (p)

*W unicornis* (p,h) – uncommon

*Entelecara erythropus* (p) – frequent in the south, less so in the north.

*Gongylidium rufipes* (h)

*Dismodicus bifrons* (p,h)

*Baryphyma pratense* (h) – first record for Perthshire. Rare in Scotland. Recorded mainly in wet areas.

*B trifrons* (h)

*Gonatium rubens* (p,h)

*Maso sundevalli* (h)

*Peponocranium ludicrum* (p,h)

*Pocadicnemis pumila* (p,h)

*Hypselistes jacksoni* (p,h) – rather rare and usually in wet habitat.

*Oedothorax gibbosus* (h) – common in damp places.

*Pelecopsis mengei* (h) – local in damp places.

*Cnephalocotes obscurus* (p,h) – local.

*Minyriolus pusillus* (p,h)

*Tapinocyba pallens* (p,h) – local.

*Monocephalus fuscipes* (p,h)

*Gongylidiellum vivum* (p) – common in damp habitat.

*Micrargus herbigradus* (p,h)

*M apertus* (h)

*Erigonella hiemalis* (p,h)

*Savignia frontata* (h)

*Diplocephalus picinus* (h) – local in wet areas.

*Erigone dentipalpis* (h)

*E atra* (h)

*Aphileta misera* (h) – local.
*Porrhomma pygmaeum* (p,h)
*Agyneta conigera* (h)
*A ramosa* (p,h) – infrequent in damp habitat.
*Centromerus sylvaticus* (p)
*C arcanus* (p,h) – less common.
*C dilutus* (p,h)
*Centromerita bicolor* (p)
*C concinna* (p)
*Sintula corniger* (p,h) – uncommon in Scotland.
*Saaristoa abnormis* (p)
*Bathyphantes gracilis* (h)
*B parvulus* (p,h)
*Kaestneria dorsalis* (h) – Perthshire appears to be the northern limit for this species in Britain.
*K pullata* (h) – common in wet areas.
*Poeciloneta variegata* (h)
*Drapetisca socialis* (h) – inhabits tree trunks and litter at the base of trees.
*Labulla thoracica* (h)
*Lepthyphantes obscurus* (h)
*L tenuis* (h)
*L zimmermanni* (p,h)
*L cristatus* (p)
*L mengei* (p,h)
*L tenebricola* (h)
*L ericaeus* (p,h)
*Linyphia triangularis* (h) – a medium sized spider whose webs are very commonly seen strung on a wide variety of vegetation from mid-summer to late autumn.
*Linyphia (Neriene) montana* (h)
*L (N) clathrata* (h)
*Microlinyphia pusilla* (p,h)
*Allomengea scopigera* (h) – common in wet areas.

Order OPILIONES (Harvestmen)
The six species listed are common and have a widespread distribution.

Family NEMASTOMATIDAE
*Nemastoma bimaculatum* (p)

Family PHALANGIIDAE
*Oligolophus tridens* (p)
*Paroligolophus agrestis* (p)
*Lacinius ephippiatus* (p)
*Mitopus morio* (p)
*Rilaena triangularis* (p)

*Pardosa nigriceps*

*Tetragnatha extensa*

Photographs: Dick Jones

## DRAGONFLIES AND DAMSELFLIES –
## OPPORTUNITIES FOR FURTHER RECORDING IN THE FORTH VALLEY

Jonathan Willet

### Introduction

This paper is intended to provide a little background to Odonata (the order containing Dragonflies and Damselflies), and to suggest locations where Odonata recording could be focussed. For a full historical view of the Odonata of the Forth Area refer particularly to Smith and Smith (1999). For more information on their ecology and behaviour refer to publications in the references.

Together with the Mayflies, Dragonflies and Damselflies make up the most ancient group of insects, the Paleoptera. The Paleoptera probably evolved in the warm regions of the world about 300 million years ago (mya) during the Carboniferous period. Fossils of dragonfly-like insects were found from this period. They had wingspans of 70 cm. By 250 mya most of the modern families had evolved. There are approximately 5500 species of Odonata alive today (Miller 1995). They are most abundant in the tropics.

Out of the 5500 species of Odonata in the world, Britain has 45 species and Scotland has 21 species. Compared to the 69 species in the Netherlands and 99 species found in France, Britain does have an impoverished fauna. This is mainly due to our isolated position as an island (some Odonata will not fly over large bodies of water).

### Habitat loss

Over the UK the size of our Odonata populations has certainly declined in most areas during this century, by as much as 90 % in some places, due to the huge loss of wetland areas. Subsequently the conservation of these remaining wetland areas is very important. Global warming may also have an effect on the species found here. Southern European species may move into Britain and the more Northern species may ultimately disappear.

Locally, since the 1890s the number of small ponds (under 4 hectares in area) in the Central region has increased by 86 %. This goes against the national trend (McLusky and Lassiere 1993). During this period 188 lochs were created and 40 were lost. This compares with a 23 % loss in Midlothian and a 82 % loss in Bedfordshire, over the same period. So it seems that for the more generalist species, suitable habitat has actually increased in our area. However, it seems that our rare species have become rarer over this period.

### Dragonflies and damselflies

Dragonflies and damselflies belong to the Order Odonata. Dragonflies belong to the sub-Order Anisoptera, meaning unequal wings, which refers to the difference in size and structure of the fore and hind wings. Damselflies belong to the sub-Order Zygoptera, meaning equal wings.

Dragonflies are powerful fliers, larger and more robust than damselflies and have large eyes that meet in the middle of the head. When at rest they hold their wings flat and open at ninety degrees to their bodies.

Damselflies are weak fliers, with delicate bodies and have small eyes that do not meet in the middle, giving them a 'hammerheaded' appearance. When at rest they hold their wings closed over their abdomen. The only exception to this is the emerald damselfly *Lestes sponsa*, which holds its wings half open.

**Names**

Scottish names of dragonflies are Horse stingers or the Deil's darning needles, while in America they were known as Mosquito hawks or Horse doctors. The third name is probably the best description of all, as these fast aerial hunters do prey on small winged insects. The Gaelic for Dragonfly is *Damhan nathrach* or *Tarbh nathrach*. These literally translate as ox/stag snake and bull snake. The snake or stinger names refer to the popular, but incorrect, assumption that dragonflies bite or sting.

Common names for some dragonflies use the words darter, hawker and chaser. This refers to their flying habits. Darters dart out from a perch to catch insects whereas hawkers spot their prey whilst on the wing. Chasers patrol a territory and will chase any insect that comes into their airspace.

**Amazing numbers**

The four-spotted chaser and the black darter are both known to migrate. The four-spotted chaser has the most spectacular migrations in Europe. This species breeds in enormous numbers in the lakes of Scandinavia and Eastern Europe. Most of these migrations tend to be local in nature but sometimes they can involve long distances and huge numbers.

For example in Belgium, in June 1900 a giant cloud of dragonflies was estimated to extend over 4500 square miles. Some towns were in near darkness for more than four hours and the author of one account declined to estimate their numbers "for fear of disbelief". The largest ever recorded migration was in Germany in 1862. It was estimated to have consisted of 2,400,000,000 insects (Strange But True column, *Daily Telegraph* June 1995). These numbers may seem ridiculous but this swarming behaviour is comparable to that of locusts, which can occur in equally unbelievable numbers.

More recent, and verified, large swarms formed a cloud of dragonflies travelling within a cyclone that covered 34 square kilometres (Corbet 1999). Other instances include a migration of about one million common darters coming into Ireland in 1947. This column of dragonflies was a few metres wide and continued for several days (Corbet 1961). In Europe the last gigantic swarm was recorded in 1971, travelling through Belgium and the Netherlands, some flights extended continuously for 6 km and contained an estimated 400,000 individuals per square kilometre (Corbet 1999).

It is not known what mechanism triggers these migrations. Perhaps it is a lack of food or overcrowding in one area. Such huge migrations that "blackened the skies" may be a thing of the past due to the loss of wetland all over Europe.

## Watching Odonata

The recording of Odonata is a pretty civilized affair. Wait for a sunny summer day, with temperatures above 15 degrees Celsius, find a water body that has plenty natural emergent and marginal vegetation, sit near the edge and wait for activity. If you are feeling extra energetic you can take your socks and shoes off and go wading in the boggy or muddy margins of a loch or pond and see what flies away from you.

To watch dragonflies close up you need a pair of binoculars that can focus down to a distance of 9 feet or less, or if you are a good stalker you can try and creep up on a dragonfly that has alighted. Try to do this from the rear of the insect. It is possible to get very close (within 20 cm) by doing this. If you are fleet of hand, you can use a net to capture them. When handling any dragonflies hold them by the bases of their wings so that all four wings are held together between your forefinger and thumb. If the wings have a "soft" look to them or the wing spots at the outer leading edge of the wing are white or pale (signifying a recently emerged adult), do not handle the insect as you will damage its wings, as they have not yet fully hardened up.

These immature stages can be persuaded to climb onto your finger, especially in cooler weather, again affording a very close look at them. But as soon as they warm up from your body heat they will fly off. On cool days look in the vegetation and trees back from the edge of the water body. More often than not you will find damselflies and sometimes dragonflies roosting there.

It takes time to get your eye in for the larger dragonflies as they are usually flying quickly, but the smaller darters and chasers and the damselflies are easier to follow. The field guides available today are very good and really do make identification much easier, Brooks (1997) is excellent. Dragonflies can be found just about anywhere as they wander many kilometres from their breeding sites. I have seen a golden-ringed dragonfly at the top of a Munro and also a common hawker (I think) while hanging out my washing when I lived in Buchan. The nearest common hawker breeding site was 10 kilometres away.

When you see a dragon or damselfly you need to note its habitat, colour, markings and behaviour. From this you should be able to identify the species or at least narrow it down to two. One thing to remember is that size estimates are difficult as everyone thinks dragonflies are far larger (15-20 cm) than they really are. The golden-ringed dragonfly is our largest with a wingspan of 10 cm and a body length of 8 cm.

If you are seriously keen you can invest in a colander, white plastic spoon and hand lens. This is all you need to go looking for Odonata larvae. Use the colander as a net, the spoon to pick out larvae from the colander and the hand lens to look at the small identifying features. You will also need a larval key. This can be found in Brooks (1997), Hammond (1994) and Miller (1995).

## When to go looking

Sunny days are the obvious choice as this is when Odonata are most likely to be on the wing. Later on in this paper I give a rough guide as to when certain species of Odonata are flying. The weather plays a major part in the time of emergence of Odonata and also for how long they will be on the wing. A warm spring will mean that species will be emerging early, likewise a cold and wet autumn will reduce the flight period of most species. In general a series of hard frosts in September/ October spells the end of Odonata activity for that year.

Cool weather does not spell the end of all activity. Females of the larger species of dragonflies can stay active when temperatures are below 10 degrees Celsius, usually when they are egg laying in the morning, late in the season. Listen for the rustling of wings against vegetation. This wing beating keeps the flight muscles warm enough to stay functional.

**Where to go looking**

As already mentioned just about any water body, provided it is pollution free, has the capability of holding some species of Odonata. New ponds in urban or agricultural areas will probably be colonised by damselflies first, as they are the most common species in these areas. New ponds close to semi-natural habitats can be colonised quickly by many different species. All species of Odonata can colonise suitable, new habitat, with dragonflies tending to travel furthest. While attaining maturity dragonflies may travel several (or more) kilometres from where they emerged, Damselflies tend to travel several hundred metres or less.

To find a habitat with a fairly large assemblage of Odonata species (6 to 8) you need to look for long established ponds in designed landscapes or semi-natural water bodies, with a fair extent of unintensively managed woodland or grassland surrounding them.

Once you have found a waterbody with a good assemblage of species, keep visiting it so that you get to know the commoner species and feel confident identifying them. You will also get a feel for the habits of the various species, where you are likely to find them and what they will be up to.

Certain rare species have specific habitat requirements, these are:

**Beautiful demoiselle** – Moderate to fast flowing burns, with aquatic vegetation. Found in the Trossachs.

**Northern emerald** – Bog pools among open forest and similar pools adjacent to woodland. The most important feature of these pools is a fringe of floating Sphagnum moss. Any Sphagnum fringed pools are worth having a look at. The lowland raised bogs of the Carse are potential habitat for this species.

**Downy emerald** – Sheltered woodland ponds or lochans on east Loch Lomondside.

**Azure hawker** – Shallow Sphagnum rich pools in wet bog areas. Sheltered streamsides and woodlands close to breeding habitat are used by both sexes for hunting and basking. Upland areas.

**Recording of Odonata**

If you are keen enough to go watching Odonata you are keen enough to formally record them. After birds, plants, mammals and butterflies, Odonata are our best recorded wildlife. That said, there are very few records from our area and there are lots of ponds and waterbodies that have not been looked at for their Odonata. There is a lot of recording still to be done. Site records for Odonata allow us to see if their distribution is changing and generally monitor their status in an area.

A formal recording scheme has been running for many years. Record cards are filled in with the date, location and a description of the species seen. The most important records are those where breeding at that site has been confirmed. This is either by observing the emergence of the winged insect from the larval case or finding the exuviae (the outer skin of the larva that is shed when the adult emerges from it) and identifying it. These record cards are sent to the Dragonfly recorder for Scotland who forwards them on to the national recording scheme. These records will be transferred to CARSE in due course.

Record cards (RA70) are available from Biological Records Centre, Centre for Ecology and Hydrology, Monks Wood, Abbots Ripton, Huntingdon, Cambs, PE17 2BR. A sheet of advice on how to fill these out is available from myself.

In the first instance these records should be sent to The Dragonfly Recorder for Scotland, Mrs E. Smith, 33 Hunter Terrace, Loanhead, Midlothian, EH20 9SJ (include an SAE).

**The status and distribution of species found in the Forth Valley**

**Zygoptera – Damselflies.**
**1.** *Calopteryx virgo* – **Beautiful demoiselle.**
This is our most beautiful member of the Odonata order. The male has a metallic blue-green body with broad dark blue wings and iridescent wing-veins. Females are metallic green with very pale brown wings. They favour moderate to fast flowing streams with sandy or gravelly bottoms. Their flight period is from the end of May to August. In our area they have been recorded on east Loch Lomondside. There was a sighting at Loch Ard several years ago. Suitable habitat in this area is worth searching for this species.
**2.** *Lestes sponsa* – **Emerald Damselfly.** (Figure 1)
The emerald damselfly male has a mainly metallic green body with blue at the top and bottom of the abdomen. The female has an all metallic green body. When at rest this species holds its wings at 45 degrees to its body. This is unlike any other locally found species. They favour a wide variety of habitats and prefer those with lots of emergent and marginal vegetation. They are on the wing from July to September. Records for this species are spread throughout the area, due to the wide variety of habitats they can inhabit. One of the most common species I have come across locally.
**3.** *Pyrrhosoma nymphula* – **Large red damselfly.**
This is the only red damselfly found in our area. The three female colour forms all have more black on their abdomen than the male. They inhabit a wide variety of habitats. They are the earliest emerging of our Odonata and can be on the wing from early May to August. Again this species is very widespread.
**4.** *Coenagrion puella* – **Azure damselfly.**
This species is very easily confused with the common blue damselfly. The male can be distinguished by the U-shaped mark it has on the second segment of its abdomen closest to its thorax. These damselflies prefer smaller sheltered ponds with plenty of emergent vegetation at low altitudes, very different from the common blue damselfly

that prefers open water habitats with little vegetation. This species is at the northern limit of its range in the UK, with only a very few sites north of Perth.

**5. *Enallagma cyathigerum* – Common blue damselfly.**
This species is the only other predominately blue damselfly found in our area. Males have club-shaped mark on the second segment of their abdomen distinguishing them from the azure damselflies. This species is one of the most widespread in the UK and will be found at much higher altitudes than the azure damselfly. The common blue is on the wing from late May to September. This species is the only species of Odonata to breed in Sheltand.

**6. *Ischnura elegans* – Blue tailed damselfly.**
This species is superficially similar to the emerald damselfly in that it has a blue second last segment on its abdomen. However the abdomen of this species is black with no iridescence to it. Females have the same pattern on their abdomen but the blue segment can be yellow-brown as well, depending on the colour form of the female. This species is an early coloniser of new ponds and is tolerant of a wide variety of water conditions. It is on the wing from May to September.

**Anisoptera – Dragonflies.**
**7. *Aeshna caerulea* – Azure hawker.**
This dragonfly is 1 cm shorter than the common hawker and has no yellow markings on its abdomen. It is found in upland areas and there are only two records from our area, both from north of the Stirling area. This species' preference for upland habitat and for only flying on sunny days mean that it is difficult to get to suitable habitat on a suitable day to see it. The flight period is from June to early August.

**8. *Aeshna juncea* – Common hawker. (Figure 3)**
This large black and blue dragonfly, with yellow markings, is the most common dragonfly that you will see in the Forth Valley. On the wing its abdomen appears more black than blue, but when at rest, which is seldom, you can see the blue marking on the abdominal segments. This species is found in the ponds and pools of both lowland and upland areas. I have recorded this species on Loch Lomondside and have also had a report of it in someone's garden in Denny. It is on the wing from late June to early October.

**9. *Cordulegaster boltonii* – Golden-ringed dragonfly.**
Unmistakable, the only large, black and yellow dragonfly found in the UK. The female is very similar to the male apart from having a pointed end to her abdomen. This point is an ovipositor (egg laying tube) that the female uses when laying her eggs in rivers or boggy runnels. It favours moorland and heathland areas mainly west of the Highland Boundary fault. There is lots of seemingly suitable habitat in the Ochils, Campsies, and along the Slamannan plateau, where it has not been recorded. Forest tracks are favourite hunting grounds for this species. I have seen one hunting over bracken in a clearing near Loch Katrine and I have been told of a sighting in the woods above Dunblane (T. Young Pers. Comm.). This species is on the wing from June to September.

**10. *Somatochlora arctica* – Northern Emerald.**
This species was recently discovered in the Trossachs, at that time, 1994, its most southerly breeding site in mainland Britain. This dragonfly has a very dark green, almost black abdomen with green eyes and thorax. It favours Sphagnum fringed bog pools, in or close to woodland. Records for this species come from east Loch Lomondside and north of the Stirling area. This species is on the wing from June to September.

**11. *Cordulia aenea* – Downy emerald.**
This species is only recorded from two sites in our area, both on east Loch Lomondside. One of the two sites was created five years ago, so potentially the lack of

suitable habitat is keeping this species very localised. This dragonfly has a greenish-bronze abdomen and a downy metallic green thorax. It favours sheltered woodland ponds or lochans. This species is on the wing from mid-May to mid-July.

**12. *Libellula quadrimaculata* – Four-spotted chaser**
This species is the first dragonfly to be found on the wing in our area. It can be seen from May onwards till August. It is most common in the west of the Forth valley but is a noted migrant. It favours still water habitats from sea level to upland areas. This dragonfly has an all brown abdomen and thorax. The abdomen tapers towards the end.

**13. *Sympetrum striolatum* – Common darter.** (Figure 2)
This species has been recorded in Bannockburn and the Trossachs, but it must be in the surrounding areas. It appears that over the last 20 years this species has been slowly moving west and north. The reasons for this expansion are unknown. The stronghold of this species, in Scotland, is west of the Highland boundary fault. It is not known if this population is expanding south and east. The male of this dragonfly has a red abdomen with a brown and yellow thorax, the immatures and females have a yellow to light brown abdomen.

**14. *Sympetrum danae* – Black darter.** (Figure 4)
The black darter is the smallest of our dragonflies. It is on the wing from mid-July to October. It is a common moorland and heathland species but has not been recorded on the Braes of Doune or the Campsie and Gargunnock hills. It is also found in ponds and lochs where there are plenty emergent rushes and sedges. Males are predominately black with yellow spots on their abdomen. These spots disappear as the insect ages. Immatures are yellow, females become olive-coloured with age.

**15. *Anax imperator* – Emperor dragonfly.**
This species is a bit of an enigma. It has been recorded officially only once in Scotland, several immatures emerging from a garden pond in Edinburgh. It was thought to have been transported from England on aquatic plants. The distribution map for this species shows that its northern limit is a line stretching from the Wirral to the Humber. There are local records of this species on Loch Lomondside and from Dunmore. So keep your eyes peeled. It has been suggested that this species may be extending its range naturally but it seems more likely that it has been brought to our area on aquatic plants originating in England.

The dragonfly itself is unmistakable, the male has an apple green thorax with a blue abdomen with black lines along the top. The female has a green abdomen with similar markings. It is on the wing from June to late August.

## References
Brooks, S. (1997). *Field Guide to the Dragonflies and Damselflies of Great Britain and Ireland.* British Wildlife Publishing. Rotherwick. (Best field guide available).

Brown, L. (2000). *Dragonflies and Damselflies of the Forth Valley.* CARSE. Stirling. (Overview of local occurrence of Odonata, available from the Smith Art Gallery and Museum).

Corbet, P. S. (1999). *Dragonflies: Behaviour and Ecology of Odonata.* Harley Books. Colchester. (The most up to date, detailed and comprehensive publication covering all aspects of Odonata)

Corbet. P.S, Longfield. C and Moore. N. W. (1961 – reprinted 1985). *Dragonflies.* Collins New Naturalist. London. (Detailed account of the biology and behaviour of Odonata worldwide).

Hammond, C. O. (1994) *The Dragonflies of Great Britain and Ireland.* 3rd impression. Harley Books. Colchester. (Excellent larval key and now out of date distribution maps)

McLusky, D. S. and Lassiere, O. (1993) Aquatic Life: Lochs, Rivers, Estuaries. *In Central Scotland – land, wildlife, people* (editor Corbett, L.) pp. 90-106. Forth Naturalist and Historian. Stirling.

64  *Jonathan Willet*

Merritt. R, Moore. N. W and Eversham. B. C. (1996). *Atlas of the Dragonflies of Britain and Ireland.* ITE research publication no.9. HMSO. London. (First national atlas of Odonata).

Miller. P. L. (1995). *Dragonflies.* Naturalists Handbook no. 7. The Richmond Publishing Co.Ltd. Slough. (Concise but detailed account of all aspects of UK Odonata's biology and behaviour).

Smith, E. M. and Smith, R. W. J. (1999) The Odonata (Dragonflies) of the Forth Area. *Forth Naturalist and Historian* 22, pp. 55-59.

Figure 1
Emerald damselfly (male)
*Lestes sponsa*

Figure 2
Common darter (male)
*Sympetrum striolatum*

Figure 3
egg laying
Common hawker (female)
*Aeshna juncea*

Figure 4
Black darter (male)
*Sympetrum danae*

## MANAGEMENT OF HERMITAGE WOOD, STIRLING UNIVERSITY

Chris Perkins

Hermitage Wood has a semi natural woodland flora. Woodland has existed on this site for over 300 years and has a long history of management. The first major landscape alterations are attributed to Robert Haldane (Mackay and Angus 1984). These alterations were carried out in the 1790s, and included the planting of exotic trees and the transplanting of 80 year old mature trees. The woods were managed well into this century for shooting purposes, the rights for which subsidised woodland management.

The 'Great Blow' of 1968 was responsible for 40 % of the wood being blown down. This necessitated major clearance and replanting, and also allowed a great deal of regeneration.

In 1971 the north east corner of the wood was replanted with oak, alder, poplar and scots pine. The aim was to establish a study area for assessing the effects of trees on both the site and ground vegetation. In the mid 1970s a large number of mature and semi-mature elm trees were killed by an outbreak of Dutch Elm Disease (Neiland and Shepherd 1990), and had to be removed in sanitation fellings.

When new management of the wood began in 1999, the most significant threat was the spread of invasive species. The extent was such that the native character of the wood was severely threatened, and it is well on the way to becoming an exotic plantation rather than a semi natural woodland. Rhododendron had spread throughout the wood. Sycamore was the dominant species in all age classes, comprised 67 % of the stems, and was the majority of the natural regeneration. The table below demonstrates the distribution of species throughout the wood.

*% Species Distribution All Compartments*

| Ash | 17 | Lime | 5 |
|---|---|---|---|
| Birch | 1 | Lodge pole | 1 |
| Beech | 2 | Sessile oak | 1 |
| Dead ash | 1 | Ped oak | 1 |
| Dead elm | 2 | Sitka | 1 |
| Elm | 2 | Sycamore | 67 |

It was unrealistic to remove all of the sycamore from the wood, so areas of mature trees were identified and felled. These areas were restocked with native trees, matched to the ground conditions. Natural regeneration would have been the preferred method of restocking, but this would have resulted in more sycamore. The areas were replanted at a relatively high stocking density to ensure that a dense canopy forms and shades out any future sycamore seedlings.

Two small conifer plantations were removed from the wood at the same time as the sycamore felling.

A second operation took place in the summer of 2001 to remove rhododendron and sycamore seedlings.

Rhododendron was present throughout the wood. As part of a four year contract, it was cut in summer 2001. It will be sprayed for the next three years to ensure that it does not re-colonise the site.

Sycamore seedlings and saplings were removed from the wood in the same operation. In many areas sycamore and ash regeneration has grown in the gaps left from 'Big Blow' and the removal of diseased elms in the 1970s. The removal of the sycamore saplings has increased the percentage of native species.

Work will continue in the next few years, with the spraying of sycamore and rhododendron stumps, and of sycamore regeneration. The wood will be monitored, and should be on the road to recovery.

Hermitage Wood may never be a pure native woodland, and the work carried out to date is not intended to make it so. The management now is intended to alter the dynamics and prevent it from turning into a sycamore and rhododendron wood.

*References and Further Reading*

Angus, David and L. Corbett. 1986 and 1995. *Airthrey and Bridge of Allan*. Forth Naturalist and Historian. 32pp. including for Hermitage Wood some history geology, map, illustrations – reduced price £1.

Hudson, L. 1994. Hermitage wood, a woodland conservation project. *Staneybreaks* (Stirling Civic Trust), vol 1 no 2, pp16-20.

Mackay, K.J.H. and David Angus. 1984. *Airthrey Roads: Captain Haldane's Magic Roundabout*. Forth Naturalist and Historian. 32pp. £1.50.

MacLean, Ella. 1974. *The Airthrey Estate: a Visitor's Guide*. Airthrey Gardens Group. op.

Neiland, Ruth, and J.W. Shepherd. 1990. Dutch elm disease in central Scotland. *Forth Naturalist and Historian* 12, 53-66. – this is a follow up on the E.N. Greensill paper of the same title in 1977, ibid 2,71-8.

**Bill Brackenbridge (1952-2000), FNH Board Member**           **L. Corbett**
    The tragic car accident in Aviemore just before our symposium last
November robbed central Scotland of a greatly respected naturalist and
committed environmentalist long associated with FNH and environmental
education eg the annual Green Scene of the forum CREEF now MSEEF, also the
Young Forth Naturalist awards series in the five Man and the Landscape
symposia from 1987, particularly the second 'The Mighty Oak', here
photographed in the *Stirling Observer*, with Bill on the left, veteran David
Steven, centre, and the Shieldhall primary school project team.
    Some of his more substantial achievements include – the conversion of an
old quarry into the Doune Ponds reserve; persuading the owner of Cambus
Pool to make it into a Local Nature Reserve; the setting up, developing,
managing, the outstanding biodiverse Jupiter Wildlife Garden from derelict
ICI land in Grangemouth; with BRISC in 1980 setting up the Stirling Biological
Record centre, now the thriving CARSE at the Smith Art Gallery and Museum.
Doing an MSc at Stirling he joined, as Ecologist, Brian Thomson's North
Lanarkshire Conservation and Greening at Palacerigg (once the haunt of David
Steven!); he was a key man in butterfly conservation; a great bird man – and
bird imitator; a first class naturalist artist; active in many naturalist
organisations and projects eg the Millennium Atlas of Butterflies, even in the
proposed redevelopment of Ravenscraig.
    His loss has been notably recorded by SWT, Butterfly Conservation and
others, and via Brian Thomson RSPB is hosting a fund for a possible 'living
memorial' bird habitat or nature reserve. He was a great help in FNH, not least
to Cliff Henty in producing our annual Forth Bird Report.

Photograph by Van der Merwe.

## BOOK REVIEWS

**Loch Lomond: a Special Place.** A collection of invited papers in *Scottish Geographical Journal* 116, pt3, 2000, pp177-270.

Papers by Hansom, Maitland, Adams, Mitchell et al on – natural heritage, importance, water management, lakeshore erosion, recreational use, boating effects.

**Loch Lomondside. Gateway to the Western Highlands of Scotland.** John Mitchell. New Naturalist, Harper Collins. 232pp. 0 00 220146 1. £14.99 pbk £34.99 Hbk.

A sweeping, authoritative survey by Nature Conservancy's ambassador for the district. 35 years intimacy with its ecology, history, wildlife are here distilled into this latest New Naturalist series volume, giving 30pp on the physical environment – rocks, landscape, weather; 40 on the influence of man – from the hunter gatherer times, forestry agriculture fisheries, industry water power, sport recreation; 90pp on wildlife, habitats, communities, species – of the loch, lowlands, muirs and mountains. Then conservation matters – past present future, as at long last the area becomes Scotland's first national park. Aimed at the general reader it is well illustrated and referenced.

**The Millennium Atlas of Butterflies in Britain and Ireland.** J Asher et al. Butterfly Conservation / OUP 464pp. 0 19 850865 5. £30 hbk.

A full-colour feast of photography documenting five years of knowledgeable recording by thousands of volunteers. This is the current assessment of our butterflies, their habitats, changes, and the threats they face, since the previous atlas of 1984. All species have detailed accounts and distributions, long term trends, new ecology; European changes are considered, and a vision given of how these popular insects might be conserved in the future.

**Birdnews,** PO box 740, Norwich NR2 3SH

A new reporting, alerting service see www.birdnews co.uk

**Loch Lomond and the Trossachs National Park. Draft Statutary Order.** (170pp.) – 27pp text 140pp of maps of areas and boundaries

For final consultations – submissions by 21 September 2001. Still expanded into Argyll, excludes Killin, has full planning authority.

**Scotland's Environment: the Future.** Editors George Holmes and Roger Crofts. Tuckwell /RSE / SNH. 160pp. 1 86232 162 0. £14.99.

Distinguished contributors look at changes in environment and land use over the centuries and promote an 'agenda for action'. It seems rather bland, surprisingly not stressing 'biodiversity' now the 'in word' of world and local environment projects.

# 'FORTY YEARS ON':
## STIRLING FIELD and ARCHAEOLOGICAL SOCIETY

### K.J.H. Mackay

Regular readers of the *Forth Naturalist & Historian* (FNH) will perhaps recall the Editorial of Volume 3 (1978), celebrating the Centenary of the Stirling Field Club. The publication of its *Transactions* over the period from 1878 to 1939 set the pattern taken on by FNH from 1976, in putting in print some presentations of the annual *'Man and the Landscape'* symposia and many other contributions to the history and natural history of the Forth area.

Stirling Field Club saw its name changing to the more respect-inspiring 'Stirling Natural History and Archaeological Society' (SNHAS) in 1882, under pressure from John Murray, Secretary of the 'Challenger' Reports (later <u>Sir</u> John). Throughout the passing years, members of the Society made impressive contributions to the growth in knowledge of the natural world, a fact which produces a feeling of some awe on the part of present members. Currently it rejoices in the title of the Stirling Field and Archaeological Society (SFAS), adopted at its revival in 1961 following dormancy during and immediately after the Second World War. Last year's SFAS Committee, realising the approach of the 40th anniversary of the inaugural meeting of the resuscitated Society, resolved to commemorate this in some suitable manner. (This would also celebrate the 123rd anniversary of the Stirling Field Club.) The hope was that, after forty years, it would be reasonably easy to persuade any of the original re-formers still in circulation to join us in our celebrations, and give us their recollections of the early days.

Our festivities were planned to take place at the Smith Museum and Art Gallery on Tuesday, 13th March 2001, following an abbreviated AGM. The 'Forty Years On' Exhibition would be opened by our Honorary President, J.K.Thomson, himself Secretary at the time of re-formation of the Society. Thereafter a 'cheese and wine' type reception would allow members and friends to mix socially, leading to the climax, a celebratory cake-cutting. In the event, we were delighted to have among our guests A.B. Cruickshank and B. Weld from the Steering Committee of 40 years ago, and our hard-working Secretary (and Treasurer) for thirty-five of those years, Dorothy Milne.

The Exhibition, in the Ballengeich Room at the Smith, aimed to highlight key facets of the Society' activities. Two display cabinets and nine large wall panels gave adequate space to develop aspects of these topics without overwhelming the visitor. It was difficult to give full emphasis to the early interests and achievements of Society members, but enough was available to refresh the memories of senior members, while there was a good selection of more recent activities to attract interested members of the public to consider joining us. Over the four weeks that the Exhibition was on display, it attracted a lot of interest, and many visitors made a return visit to study the displays at their own pace.

The 'field' aspects highlit ornithology (bird-ringing and migration studies, and nest-boxes) and mountain flora. A collection of the tools of the bird-ringer's trade was embellished with a few bird specimens from the Museum's shelves, while a red squirrel investigated a prominently numbered bird-box. The display panels showed colour photos of the research-workers in the field, and graphed their principal results. The mountain flora panel paid tribute to our late doyenne of botanists, Margaret Hargreave.

Archaeology always features largely in our lecture programme, and many of our members like to know of digs going on in the neighbourhood, either to visit or to volunteer their services as excavators. One of the early finds made during an SFAS dig was exhibited, a Bronze Age food-vessel discovered in a burial cist in Coneypark in 1971. Wall panels gave details of some 33 sites on which, over the past 40 years, SFAS members had made valued contributions. A range of the resulting published work was also on display, through journals such as *Discovery & Excavation in Scotland*, the *Proceedings of the Society of Antiquaries of Scotland*, and – of course – the *Forth Naturalist and Historian*.

Three further panels presented visual records of 'Expeditions and Excursions', research results in the 'Local History' sphere and 'Highlights of the past 40 Years'. We were reminded that the SFAS had played a pivotal role in the 'Save the Smith' Campaign of 1968-73, had fought a gallant rearguard action in the 'Save the Bastion' battle of 1971-72, and had enjoyed a nation-wide success with the Lottery Funding of the Barnwell Commemoration Flight in 1999.

A section of one display case dealt with publications … the SFAS Newsletter, our earlier Transactions, samples of the *Forth Naturalist and Historian*, and copies of journals exchanged with our corresponding society in Stirling's twin town in France, Villeneuve d'Ascq. Our members are involved in individual publications, *Border Towers*, *Stirling Churches* and a recent series of Archaeological Leaflets being produced in conjunction with the Stirling-Smith.

It is appropriate that the final reference is devoted to an exhibit loaned by our newest associates, the Stirling branch of the Young Archaeologists' Club, which is – while only two years old – making its mark. A field-walking session enabled two keen-eyed young archaeologists to spot a stone lamp which may date back 3,000 years!

The last forty years has seen the SFAS serving the diverse interests of its members in an informal structure which encourages cross-subject interest. Time alone will tell whether increased specialisation at the professional level will spread into the world of the enthusiastic but generalist amateur and force a redefinition of our sphere of interest. We are happy that we still share so much with FNH, in this the 25th anniversary of their first publication.

Courtesy of Whylers Ltd., here in this photograph of the *Stirling Observer* of 21 March 2001, are some of the Society's past and present office-bearers:

Left to right:
Ken Mackay (Chairman 1977-88)
Dorothy Milne (Secretary 1964-98 and Treasurer 1967-98: Hon. President since 1998)
Michael Green (Chairman 1989-95)
James Thomson (Secretary of re-formed Society 1961-64: Hon. President since 1984).
Rita Barth (present Secretary and Treasurer)
Henry Robb (present Chairman)

**BOOK REVIEW**

**First Generations: the Stirling area from Mesolithic to Roman times.** Lorna Main. Stirling Council. 48pp. ISBN 1 870 542 444. £4.99.

Through the interpretation of the archaeological evidence the book tells of the first people who moved into the area now known as Stirling, and of the peoples who succeeded them, from prehistoric times up to the period of the Roman occupation. Stirling lies at a crossroads where influences from north and south, east and west, meet. What happened here is part of a wider story, extending beyond current administrative boundaries. The book looks at relevant sites and objects which throw light on where and how the people of the area lived and died, and their impact on the environment.

BOOK REVIEWS

**From Here to Sustainability: politics in the real world.** by the Real World Coalition. authors Ian Christie and Diane Warburton. Earthscan Publications. 236pp.1 85383 735 0. £8.95.

The RWC is an alliance of leading organisions nationally (including WWF ) and globally in environmental sustainability, social justice, peace and security, and democratic renewal.

There is an alarming gap between the quality of life we say we want and the one we have – this book explains why. No policy area could be more 'evidence driven' than sustainable development, yet have no sense of urgency, apparently no understanding, that to make any progress needs tackling social, economic and environment problems together not separately.

**Loch Lomondside depicted and described. 3. Early guide books for the scientific tourist.** John Mitchell. *The Glasgow Naturalist* 23, pt 5, pp 3-6.

**Bird Census Techniques.** C.J. Bibby et al. 2nd edition. Academic Press – with RSPB, Bird Life, BTO, Geoscope. 300pp. Hbk 0 12 095831 7. £35.95.

Much revised from the first edition of 1992, with new methods – contents here indicate the scope – Purpose and design, Census errors, Mapping methods, Line transects, Point counts and transects, High species, Catching and marking, Counting individual species, Counting colonial nesting flocking and migrating birds, Distribution studies, Habitat descriptions and measurement.

**Shorebirds.** Des Thompson and Ingvar Byrkjedal. Colin Baxter – World Life Library. 72pp. 1 84107 075 0. £9.

Brilliantly photographed are some of the near 200 species of waders/shorebirds, with a fresh look including diagrams of the year in their lives, a map flyways used on migration, a species table, and a new classification. The contents indicate the scope – Diverse families, Appearance, Migration and movements (including the nonstop 4350 m/7000 km American Golden Plover's), Mating and social behaviour, Food and feeding, Conservation. Thompson is with SNH, Byrkjedal University of Bergen.

**The Islands of Loch Lomond: footprints from the past.** Hannah Stirling, Gavin Arneil, Fiona Baker. 36pp. Friends of Loch Lomond. £5.

This is a well written and attractively illustrated A4 presentation to highlight the islands attractions and history, and particularly 'popularise' some of the findings of the archaeological survey carried out by Fiona Baker some years ago. The survey being an extensive specialist work of limited access (eg for reference in the Mitchell Library, Glasgow), this is an excellent and enjoyable guide to the Loch Lomond islands history and archaeology. The survey revealed very many interesting sites previously largely unknown.

## GILBERT FARM CUNNINGHAM OF ALVA:
## PRINTER, TRANSLATOR, POLYMATH
### People of the Forth (13)

David Spooner

Dr. Gilbert Farm Cunningham was a most remarkable twentieth century Scot. Indeed he was remarkable by any national standard. A printer by livelihood, he was actually rather a polymath of a very particular, now defunct, type. One only needs to study the contents of his library, some of which is in Stirling University Library, to realize the breadth of the man's reading. His enthusiasm for literature had been whetted by the great Glaswegian medievalist, W.P. Ker, under whom he had studied at London University. But as Dr. Cunningham's library shows, he ranged far and wide in a different field from two other great twentieth century Scottish polymaths, Douglas Young and D'Arcy Wentworth Thompson. Probably because of his eventual profession as a pioneer printer (about which more anon), he was closer to popular taste than either Young or D'Arcy Thompson. To say he was a lad o pairts is, I believe, to put the matter too crisply. He was rather an intellectual who always had one eye, one part of his mind, on that mythical beast, 'the common reader.' At the same time, as his bibliographical work on Dante shows, he was a most unusual, perhaps unique, committed autodidact, a lay scholar of a thoroughness to put many to shame. Such all-round intellectuals have, as I suggested earlier, become an extinct breed as a certain brand of professionalism and extremely specialized knowledge – some of it, of course, entirely necessary – have crushed the wide-ranging, although it still survives to a certain degree in Scottish Universities.

Gilbert Farm Cunningham was born in 1900 in Alva. His father, Robert, had visited Alva from Glasgow in 1889 during the Autumn Holiday with a view to setting up a print works, which he did that same year. He established it first at No 176 on the Stirling Road, and soon at No 124, before moving to a permanent base in the former weaving shop at Longbank Works in 1898 at the entrance to Alva Glen. Situated at the side of the old weaving shed, the first house constructed in Alva with more than a single storey – 'The Castle' as it was known locally – became the company's offices in 1931 where they remained until new premises were found in 1959. Indeed the surviving relative and fellow director, Charles Coull, recalls an incident there when he had to take a phone call from one of their London clients at the very moment when a shepherd was leading his sheep down from the Glen. Amazed the London businessman had to break to ask what all the bleating was at the other end of the line! Always in the forefront of printing technology of the day, the latest letterpress and automatic feeder were installed as early as the end of the Great War. Indeed one of his co-directors generously lent me a flyer advertising the fact that in 1916 Robert Cunningham & Co. had published the first book printed in Scotland using the Cyrillic alphabet. Shortly before Gilbert

Cunningham's death on August 25th, 1967, the company merged with R.&R. Clark of Edinburgh. Dr. Cunningham was apparently a highly skilled monotype operator, able to take on many troubleshooting tasks at once, and Charles Coull in conversation with me remarked that he had "an astronomical knowledge of the printing trade." I was interested to hear that the company had a number of contracts with the printers for so many years to the University of Glasgow, Robert MacLehose, with whom I had dealings when they handled printing for Borderline Press which I ran in the 1970s and 1980s, and which was originally set up to publish Tom Scott's splendid epic poem of Darwinian evolution, *The Tree*. At its height in Alva in the 1960s, the Cunningham Company employed 130 to 140 people.

However for all his practical capabilities, it is not for this he will be remembered by the international intellectual community. It is for his translations from Spanish, French, and German, although he also taught himself Italian which led to his huge Critical Bibliography of Dantean translations as well as Russian, and Latin from his schooldays. His greatest original works are his translations from Góngora's *Solidades* (*Solitudes*) and from *Polifemo*. A.A. Parker, late professor of Hispanic Studies at Edinburgh University - and author of the classic, *The Philosophy of Love in Spanish Literature* (1985) – acutely wrote of him: "Despite his activity as a translator Dr. Cunningham was not a linguist in the ordinary sense of the word. He could not really speak or write well, much less pronounce, any of the six languages which he translated. Yet he had an instinct for languages, as seen in his extraordinary flair for grasping, seemingly intuitively, the meaning of any passage of verse in these six." Bearing in mind then that the Baroque style of Góngora is difficult to translate, extremely artificial and inflected, perhaps paralleled only by some of the high-falutin flyting of Dunbar, or the latinate verses of Milton, here is Stanza 27 of *Polyphemus and Galatea* from Cunningham's version:

> Heated, he gave the stream his hands, and these
> Raised to his face and brow the cooling tide,
> Between two hoary-footed myrtle trees,
> Like green-clad heron at the current's side.
> Uncertain folds of empty draperies,
> Spread by Favonius' gentle breath, supplied
> A bed, if not a wind-swung hammock, made
> From slender couch-grass and refreshing shade.

This is splendidly done, not least the "green-clad heron" which images the "hoary-footed"-ness of the myrtles beyond the plainness of the "dos verdes garzas" (literally 'two green herons') of the Spanish.

The Spanish translations were published by Edinburgh University Press, and also the Johns Hopkins Press at the University of that name at Baltimore. Yet as his library shows, Cunningham had an especially natural affinity with lyric poetry. Clearly from the extent of his holdings of Rilke volumes, he had found in German lyric poetry something of the translucence he brings to his translations. I can only think he did not essay renditions of Rilke because of the excellence of the J.B. Leishman translations, which he owned and which have never been surpassed despite scores of later translators. He did, though, make translations of another favoured German lyric poet, Eduard Mörike. Here is his version of the Mörike poem, "Free Merchandise" which no doubt struck a chord with a printer by profession:

'Ink for sale! Who lacks ink? It's fine black ink I am selling',
Came the clear call of a boy ringing the length of the street.
Laughing he raised his bright eyes to where I sat by the window,
Then he was up in my room ere I knew what was afoot.
'Nobody sent for you, boy' – 'Oh please won't you sample my wares, sir?'
And as he spoke from his back promptly he swung round his keg.
But at the movement his coat, half tattered, fell back for a moment
Baring his shoulder which gleamed bright with the glint of a wing.
'Come, lad, let's have a look; are you also a dealer in feathers?
Cupid, you counterfeit rogue, must I unmask you forthwith?'
But, though discovered, he smiled, and touching his lips with his fingers:
'Hush, they are duty-free mum, or you'll ruin my trade!
Give me your ink-pot; I'll fill it at once, for it pays to keep friendly!'
No sooner spoken than done; then he was out in a trice.
Well, since he's taken me in, I must use his gift to advantage,
Write to my sweetheart, or else pen her a passionate song.

This slyly humourous poem is subtly rendered with a sense of the dramatic that no doubt drew on his labours in forwarding the printing and the commercial side of what had now become Robert Cunningham and Sons Ltd. His brother and co-director, John Cunningham, designed the jackets for his books, and there is a particularly attractive one for Gilbert's *Lyrics from the Russian* where the Urals appear looking very like the Ochils. The environment of Alva at their foothills must have been as much an inspiration for the Cunninghams as West Lomond Hill and its surrounds were to the Kinnesswood poet Michael Bruce.

There were also plays for radio, rather than fully developed stage plays. *The Unjust Steward* was indeed performed by BBC Radio in 1942 while Dr. Cunningham was away on active service in the war as navigator on sub patrol in West Africa. (Hence his updating of *Burton's Nautical Tables*.) For today's audience, though, his finest accomplishment in the field of drama is, I believe, his treatment of the conflict between the free-living poet, Clement Marot 'the father of French poetry,' and John Calvin in his play *The Holy City*. This section gives an indication of it:

MAROT. My good friend John, you take yourself too seriously. What good will come in the end of all this cleansing and scouring you make such a mighty work of? You cannot dam up the current of human passion for ever. You may patch here and cobble there, but sooner or later the dam will burst and sweep you away with it.
CALVIN. You are deep in one of the commonest of all errors, Clement. What you call human passion, I call original sin. It is not to be accepted as our inescapable heritage, but is to be fought with the weapon of grace which God in his mercy...
MAROT. Nay, John, I have heard that sermon, or variations of it, so often since I came here, that I know it by heart. But I much doubt whether, when you have

rooted out this said original sin, that you will have anything worth preserving for the life to come.

It's an old debate, but one that is still germane. We could swap the later Thomas Carlyle for Calvin, and put Sydney Goodsir Smith for Marot, and the duel would go like that. There is a bitter political and literary sharpness to the exchanges:

MAROT. I was saying that if you interfere over much in men's opinions, you are in danger of setting yourself up as a rival to the Holy Inquisition, and pretending to an authority, which, by your own admission, no mere man dare claim.

CALVIN. Inquisition…authority…I claim no authority but the word of God. Have a care; you are going too far…

MAROT. My dear John, it is you who are going too far. Do you remember the days when we braved hostile mobs because we stood for the right to hold our own views, in the teeth of pope and king, in defiance of anathema and persecution?

CALVIN. When we dared, you mean, to assert the truth that was in our hearts, in the midst of a deluded world.

MAROT. Nay, I have done, John…for I doubt if you and I have ever been of the same mind, even when we fought side by side. For I fought – and will fight while I have the strength left, for freedom and toleration.

CALVIN. Toleration! What has toleration to do with Christ? 'He that is not for me is against me.'

MAROT. And you fight to destroy one tyranny, only to set up another in its place. Beware, John, for if you continue in this course, the day is not far distant when the faggots will be piled up on the square out there, and a new race of martyrs led to the stake…and the lives of those who ventured to disagree with John Calvin will go up in a puff of smoke.

CALVIN. Insensate man!

MAROT. Well, they tell me that Sebastian Castellio has packed and is gone already, without waiting for the deliverance of the Council on the Song of Solomon, and I think Clement Marot had better follow him, before someone sniffs out a heretical passage in one of his psalms.

I contacted BBC Scotland last year to suggest a Radio revival for the play with perhaps one or two modernisations, but the drama department maintained that "the ideas are lively, but the dialogue style is showing its age a little, and I doubt etc. etc." A pusillanimous response in all conscience.

Rediscovering Gilbert Farm Cunningham is akin to the journey undertaken by the contemporary scholar W.G. Sebald in his localized yet universal account *The Rings of Saturn* (1995). In one of his favourite haunts, the Sailors' Reading Room in Southwold, the author immerses himself in the log book of a patrol ship anchored off the pier in 1914, and reflects how "Every time I decipher one of these entries I am astounded that a trail that has long since vanished from the air or the water remains visible here on the paper. That morning, as I closed the marbled cover of the log book, pondering the mysterious survival of the written word, I noticed lying on one side on the table a…tome that I had not seen before." This expresses something of the surprise coming upon Dr. Cunningham's phenomenal collection of Dante's works, especially of editions of *La Divina Commedia*. I have included these in the bibliography appended to this article. What is especially remarkable is that in his general collection of books, he showed little interest in the spectacular or ornate, and indeed this

Dante Collection is more a testimony to his avid interest in all books Dantean. His other books are evidence of a protean concern with all aspects of human life, and although he acquired relatively few tomes of criticism – clearly capable of knowing his own mind without prompting – the one series he collected was the still unsurpassed and concise (each one less than 100 pages) Bowes & Bowes monographs of the 1950s, commissioned under Erich Heller. Dr. Gilbert Cunningham was a true "Scottish Eccentric," to quote MacDiarmid's title for those he did not quite approve of, but wanted to reclaim. This clearly modest man from Alva, with his immense continental reading, is a polymath who never lost the popular touch in his thinking and reading.

WORKS BY GILBERT FARM CUNNINGHAM

*Burton's Four Figure Navigation Tables*, with S.M. Burton (Philip, 1963).

*The Divine Comedy in English: a critical bibliography 1782-1900 and 1901-1966.* In 2 volumes (Oliver & Boyd, 1965).
First published Alva 1954 in 3 volumes.

*Nunc Dimittis:A fantasy based on an episode in Canto XV of Dante's inferno* (Alva, 1950).

*The Unjust Steward and other plays* (Oliver & Boyd, 1951). Includes *The Holy City* and *Behind the House of Obed-edom.*

Translations:

Dante, *La divina Commedia: testo critico della Società Dantesca Italiana* (19–), 3 vols. Typescript of prose translations.
Goethe, *Translations* (Oliver & Boyd, 1949).
Góngora, *Polyphemus* (Alva, 1965).
     *Polyphemus & Galatea* (Edinburgh University, 1977).
     *Solitudes* (Alva, 1964 & Johns Hopkins University, 1968).
Horace, *An Essay and some translations* (Alva, 1935).
Lamartine, *Selections* (Alva, 1951).
*Lyrics from the Russian* (Alva, 1961).
Mörike, *Poems* (Methuen, 1959). Translated with Nora K. Cruickshank.
Jean de Sponde, *Poems of Love and Death* (Oliver & Boyd, 1964).

THE DANTE COLLECTION

The principles on which he collected his library of Dante works are those he set out in his *Critical Bibliography:*
*Thanks to the labours of Paget Toynbee and others, the task of preparing a complete list of English versions of La Divina Commedia was not difficult. To collect the books themselves was not so easy. The object is to present the fullest possible array of facts regarding the English translators of the Divine Comedy.*
He also collected French and German as well as original Italian editions.

Editions of the full three sections of *LA DIVINA COMMEDIA*
(in chronological order)

| | |
|---|---|
| 1820-21 | G. Biagioli (Giovanni Silvestra: Milan). |
| 1820-22 | P. Baldassare Lombardi (Romanis: Rome). |
| 1824 | J.C. Tarver (Knight: London). |
| 1824-26 | Paul Th. Hoffmann (Deutsh Buch: Berlin). |
| 1829&1849 | Philalethes von Saschen (Borngräber: Berlin). |
| 1845 | I.C. Wright (Longman: London). |
| 1849 | Artaud de Montor (Didot: Paris). |
| 1854&1887-90 | A. Pollock (Chapman & Hall: London). |
| 1856 | E. Aroux (Renouard: Paris). |
| 1856-60 | Louis Ratisbonne (Lévy: Paris). |
| 1858 | C.G. Warren Lord Vernon (Boone: London). |
| 1862 | Karl Witte (Ridolfo Decker: Berlin). |
| 1862 | J.W. Thomas (Bohn: London). |
| 1863 | Brunone Bianchi (Felice Le Monnier: Florence). |
| 1870 | Enrico C. Barlow (no publisher: London). |
| 1870 | James Ford (Smith, Elder & Co.: London). |
| 1887&1899 | Frederick K.H. Haselfoot (Duckworth: London). |
| 1889 | Pietro Fraticelli (G. Bartèra: Florence). |
| 1890 | Longfellow (Routledge: London). |
| 1890& 1899 | E.H. Plumptre (Isbister: London). |
| 1890 | Paget Toynbee (Methuen: London). |
| 1891 | I.C. Wright (George Bell: London). |
| 1892 | C.L. Shadwell (Macmillan: London). |
| 1899&1949 | Giovanni A. Scartazzini (Ulrico Hoepli: Milan). |
| 1902 | Charles Eliot Norton (Macmillan: London). |
| 1904 | Edward C. Lowe (The Minster Press: Ely). |
| 1904 | C. Potter (Digby, Long: London). |
| 1904 | H.F. Tozer (Clarendon: Oxford). |
| 1907 | Karl Vosler (Koehler: Leipzig). |
| 1909 | Robert Culley (no publisher: London). |
| 1910 | John A. Carlyle (George Bell: London). |
| 1910 | Henry F. Cary (Dent: London) and another edition (Henry Frowde: London). |
| 1911&1914 | Charles Hall Grandgent (D.C. Heath: Boston). |
| 1911 | C.E. Wheeler (Dent: London). |
| 1913 | Mario Foresi (Adriano Salani: Florence). |
| 1914 | E.M. Shaw (Constable: London). |
| 1918 | Courtney Langdon (Harvard University: Cambridge, Mass.). |
| 1921,1932&1959 | Melville B. Anderson (OUP: London). |
| 1921 | Karl Witte (Askanischer: Berlin). |
| 1922 | Otto Gildemeister (Hädecke: Stuttgart). |
| 1922 | Stefan George (Bondi: Berlin). |
| 1927 | David James Mackenzie (Longman, Green: London). |
| 1933 | Jefferson Butler Fletcher (Macmillan: New York). |

| | |
|---|---|
| 1938 | R.T. Bodey (Harold Cleaver: Bath). |
| 1938 | Oscar Hecker (Böhlans: Weimar). |
| 1939-46 | John D. Sinclair (Bodley Head: London). |
| 1943 | Hans Geisow (Hädecke: Stuttgart). |
| 1945 | Karl Vossler (Atlanta: Zürich). |
| 1946 | Theophil Spoerri (Füssli: Zürich). |
| 1946 | Temple Classics, no editor (Dent: London). |
| 1946-48 | Onorato Castellino (Società Editrice Torinese: Turin). |
| 1946-50 | Ercole Rivalta (Vallecchi: Florence). |
| 1947 | Konrad Falke (Rascher: Zürich). |
| 1948 | Patrick Cummins (Herder: St. Louis). |
| 1947 | Hermann Moge (Chamier: Freiburg). |
| 1948 | Attilio Momigliano (Sansoni: Florence). |
| 1948 | Marquès de Molins (Aguilar: Madrid). |
| 1949-1953 | Harry Morgan Ayres (Vanni: New York). |
| 1949-50 | Alexandre Masseron (Albin Michel: Paris). |
| 1949-62 | Dorothy Sayers (Penguin: Harmondsworth). |
| 1951 | Henri Longnon (Garnier: Paris). |
| 1951 | Francesco Torraca (Albrighi, Segati: Rome). |
| 1952 | S.A. Barbi (Sansoni: Florence). |
| 1952 | Edmund Th. Kauer (Droemersche: Munich). |
| 1954 | H.R. Huse (Rinehart: New York). |
| 1954 | John Ciardi (Mentor: New York & Rutgers University Press: New Brunswick). |
| 1955 | Geoffrey L. Bickersteth (Aberdeen University: Aberdeen). |
| 1956 | Glen Levin Swigget (University of the South: Sewanee). |
| 1958&1965 | R. Lillie (Cassell: London). |
| 1962 | Clara Stillman Reed (no publisher: Wilbraham, Mass.). |
| 1964 | Manfredi Porena (Zanichelli: Bologna). |
| 1964 | Giuseppe Vandelli (Ulrico Hoepli: Milan). |
| 1965 | Geoffrey L. Bickersteth (Blackwell: Oxford). |
| 1965 | William F. Ennis (Campo Editore: Florence). |
| 1965/1968 | Mary Prentice Lillie (Olympic: New York) & (Grabhorn: San Francisco). |
| n.d. | Rudolf Borchardt (Bremer: Berlin). |

## SINGLE BOOKS OF THE COMEDY

| | |
|---|---|
| 1776 *Inferno* | M. de Claifons (Clerc, Boucher: Paris). |
| 1861 *Inferno* | G. Doré (Parigini: Paris). |
| 1866 *Inferno* | William P. Wilkie (Edmonston & Douglas: Edinburgh). |
| 1877 *Inferno* | Charles Tomlinson (Partridge: London). |
| 1881 *Inferno* | Warburton Pike (Kegan Paul: London). |
| 1884 *Inferno* | James Romanes Sibbald (David Douglas: Edinburgh). |
| 1892 *Inferno* | Arthur John Butler (Macmillan: London). |
| 1893 *Inferno* | George Musgrave (Swan Sonnenschein: London). |

| | |
|---|---|
| 1894 *Inferno* | Robert Urquhart (no publisher). |
| 1895 *Inferno* | Edward Sullivan (Stock: London). |
| 1898 *Inferno* | Eugene Lee-Hamilton (Grant Richards: London). |
| 1908 *Inferno* | S.W. Griffith (Angus & Robertson: Sydney). |
| 1928 *Inferno* | Fowler Wright (Wright: London). |
| 1931 *Inferno* | Lacy Lockert (Princeton University: Princeton). |
| 1933 *Inferno* | Laurence Binyon (Macmillan: London). |
| 1933 *Inferno* | George Musgrave (OUP: London). |
| 1948 *Inferno* | Thomas G. Bergin (Appleton-Century-Crofts: New York). |
| 1961 *Inferno* | Warwick Chipman (OUP: London). |
| 1965 *Inferno* | Ronald Bottrall (CUP; Cambridge). |
| 1966 *Inferno* | Edited by, Terence Tiller (BBC: London). |
| 1883 *Purgatory* | W.S. Dugdale (George Bell: London). |
| 1901 *Purgatory* | Samuel Home (Caxton: Oswestry). |
| 1905 *Purgatory* | C.G. Wright (Methuen: London). |
| 1910 *Purgatory* | A.L. Money (George Allen: London). |
| 1911 *Purgatory* | C.E. Butler (Dent: London). |
| 1964 *Purgatory* | Hassan Osman into Arabic (Dar Al Maaref: Cairo). |
| 1900 *Paradise* | Rose Emily Selfe (Cassell: London). |
| 1947 *Paradise* | Philippe Guiberteau (Editions Claires: Paris). |
| 1952 *Paradise* | Georgina Grace Moncrieff (Moray Press: Edinburgh). |
| 1952 *Paradise* | T.W. Ramsey (Hand & Flower: Aldington). |

SELECTIONS

| | |
|---|---|
| 1860 *Selections* | E.C. Barlow (no publisher: London). |
| 1896 *Cantos* | C. Potter (Digby, Long: London). |
| 1904 *The vision of Purgatory and Paradise* | H.F. Cary (Cassell: London). |
| 1913 *Selections* | Gauntlett Chaplin (James Clarke: London). |
| 1926 *Selections* | T.W. Duncan (Heath Cranton: London). |
| 1950 *Durchblick & Auswahl* | August Vezin (Herder: Freiburg). |
| n.d. *Testo Critico della Società Dantesca Italiana* | |

OTHER

| | |
|---|---|
| 1856&1894 *Opere Minori* | Pietro Fraticelli (Barbèra: Florence). |
| 1879 *De Monarchia* | R.W. Church (Macmillan: London). |
| 1895 *Vita Nuova* | Charles Stuart Boswell (Kegan Paul: London). |
| 1902 *Vita Nuova* | D.G. Rossetti (Roux & Viarengo: Turin). |
| 1904&1924 *Tutte Le Opere,* | E. Moore & Toynbee, P. (Oxford: Nella Stampería dell'Università). |
| 1905 *Italian Poets Chiefly Before Dante* | D.G. Rossetti (Shakespeare Head: Stratford-on-Avon, 1905). |

| | |
|---|---|
| 1909 *Convivio* | W.W. Jackson (Clarendon: Oxford). |
| 1909 *Dante & Collected Verse* | G.L. Raymond (Putnam's: New York). |
| 1912 *Poetical Works* | A. Zoozmann (Herder: Freiburg). |
| 1917 *Selections from Italian Prose* | Ernesto Grillo (Blackie: London). |
| 1921 *Le Opere* | M. Barbi (Bemporad & Figlio: Florence). |
| 1930 *Choix de Poésies* | Maxime Formont (Lemerre: Paris). |
| 1943 *Das Neue Leben* | Hans Geisow (Hädecke: Stuttgart). |
| 1949 *La Consolation* | André Fraigneau (Audin: Paris). |
| 1950 *La Vita Nuova* | Tommaso Casini (Sansoni: Florence). |
| 1963 *The Odes* | H.S. Vere-Hodge (Clarendon: Oxford). |
| n.d. *Convivio* | Temple Classics (Dent: London) |
| n.d. *Das Neue Leben* | Karl Federn (Hendel: Halle). |
| n.d. *Vita Nuova* | Robert Vivier (Editions Labor: Brussels). |

## THE CRITICISM

Barbi, M., *Dante* (Sansoni: Florence, 1952).
Barbi, M., *Problemi di Critica Dantesca* (Sansoni: Florence, 1934-41). 2 vols.
Baynes, Herbert, *Dante and his Ideal* (Swan Sonnenschein: London, 1891)
Bergin, T., *An Approach to Dante* (Bodley Head: London, 1965).
*Bibliografia Dantesca* (Olschki: Florence, 1931-37). 2 vols.
Bickersteth, G.L., *On Translating Dante* (Sherratt & Hughes: Manchester, 1934).
  Botta,Vincenzo, *Study of Dante* (Slark: London, 1887).
Browning, Oscar, *Dante* (Swan Sonnenschein: London, 1891).
Carducci, G., *Dante* (Zanichelli: Bologna, n.d.).
Carroll, John S., *Exiles of Eternity: the Inferno* (Hodder & Stoughton: London, 1903)
Carroll, J.S., *In Patria: Dante's Paradiso* (Hodder & Stoughton: London, 1911).
Carroll, J.S., *Prisoners of Hope: Dante's Purgatorio* (Hodder & Stoughton: London, 1906).
Ciardi, John et al., *Dante: three lectures* (Library of Congress: Washington, 1965).
Cippico, Antonio et al., *Dante Commemoration Essays* (University of London: London, 1921).
Coles, Rosemary A., *Dante's Garden* (Methuen: London, 1898).
*A Concordance to the Divine Comedy* (Belknap: Cambridge, Mass., 1965).
Cosmo, Umberto, *Handbook* (Blackwell: Oxford, 1950).
Croce, *La Poesia di Dante* (Laterza & Figli: Bari, 1921).
Croce, *The Poetry of Dante* (Allen & Unwin: London, 1922).
Curtayne, Alice, *A Recall to Dante* (Sheed & Ward: London, 1932).
*Dante Society Lectures* (Athenaeum: London, 1906).
*Dante Society Lectures* (Pall Mall Press: London, 1909).
d'Entrèves, A.P., *Dante as a Political Thinker* (Clarendon: Oxford, 1952).
De Salvio, Alfonso, *The Rhyme Words in the Dante Commedia* (Champion: Paris, 1929).

de Sua, W.J., *Dante into English* (University of North Carolina: Chapel Hill, 1964).
Durant, H., *Dante: A Poem* (Kegan Paul: London, 1889).
Farinelli, A., *Dante* (Bocca: Turin, 1922).
Federn, Karl, *Dante* (Seeman:Leipzig, Berlin & Vienna, 1899).
Federn, K., *Dante and His Time* (Heinemann: London, 1902).
Friederich, W.P., *Dante's Fame Abroad* (Edizioni di Storia e Litteratura: Rome, 1950).
Gardner, Edmund G., *Dante* (British Academy: London, 1921).
Gardner, E.G., *Dante* (Dent: London, 1923).
Gardner, E.G., *Dante and the Mystics* (Dent: London, 1913).
Gardner, E.G., *Dante's Ten Heavens* (Constable: London, 1900).
Garnett, Richard, *Dante, Petrarch, Camoens* (John Lane: London, 1896).
Garrod, H.B., *Dante, Goethe's Faust and other lectures* (Macmillan: London, 1913).
Gaspary, A., *The History of Early Italian Literature* (no publisher: London, 1901).
Gilbert, Allan, *Dante and his Comedy* (New York University: New York, 1963).
Gilbert, A., *Dante* (Italica offprint, 1966).
Gilson, E., *Dante the Philosopher* (Sheed & Ward: London, 1948).
Grandgent, C.H., *The Power of Dante* (Harrap: London, 1918).
Gray, Nicolette, *Rossetti, Dante and Ourselves* (Faber: London, 1947).
F. Groppi, *Dante Traduttare* (Vatican: Rome, 1950).
Gustarelli, A., *Dizionario Dantesco* (Malfasi: Milan, 1946).
Harrower, R.B., *A New Theory of Dante's Matelda* (University Press: Cambridge, 1926).
Henderson, Henry F., *The Dream of Dante* (Oliphant, Anderson & Ferrer: Edinburgh, 1903).
Hensman, Mary, *A Dante Map* (Nutt: London, 1892).
Hettinger, Franz, *Dante's Divina Commedia* (Burns & Oates: London, 1887).
Hettinger, Franz, *Dante's Divina Commedia* (Burns & Oates: London, 1887).
Hunt, Leigh *Dante's Divine Comedy* (Newnes: London, n.d.).
King, R.W., *H.F. Cary [translator]* (Secker: London, 1925).
Kuhns, L. Oscar, *The Treatment of Nature in Dante's 'Divina Commedia'* (Arnold: London, 1897.)
La Piano, Angelina, *Dante's American Pilgrimage* (Yale University: New Haven, 1948).
Leigh, G., *New Light on the Youth of Dante* (Faber: London, 1929).
Leigh, G., *The Passing of Beatrice* (Faber: London, 1932).
Montano, R., *Suggerimenti per una lettura di Dante* (Conte: Naples, n.d.).
Moore, Edward, *Dante and his early biographers* (Rivington: London, 1890).
Moore, E., *Textual Criticism* (University Press: Cambridge, 1889).
Moore, E., *Studies in Dante* (Clarendon: Oxford, 1899). 2nd series.
Moore, E., *Studies in Dante* (Clarendon: Oxford, 1903). 3rd series.
Moore, E., *Studies in Dante* (Clarendon: Oxford, 1917). 4th series.
Ostermann, Theodor, *Dante in Deutschland* (Winters: Heidelberg, 1929).
Perini, N., *Lectures on Dante* (Hachette: London, n.d.).

Phillimore, C.M.,*Dante at Ravenna* (E. Stock: London, 1898).
Plumptre, E.H.,*The Life of Dante* (Isbister: London, 1900).
Raymond, G.L., *Dante & Collected Verse* (Putnam's: New York & London, 1909).
Reade, W.H.V., *Dante's Vision of History* (British Academy: London, 1939).
Ricordi, *Il Secolo di Dante* (1830). 2 vols.
Riedisser, I., *Inscriptions from the Divine Comedy* (Alfieri & Lacroix: Milan, 1913).
Rimario de 'La Divina Commedia* (Società Editrice Internazionale: Turin, 1937).
Rossetti, Maria F., *A Shadow of Dante* (Rivingtons: London, 1910).
Scartazzini, Giovanni A., *Dante* (Rütten & Loening: Frankfurt, 1879).
Scarazzini, G.A., *A Companion to Dante* (Macmillan: London, 1893)
Scartazzini, G.A., *A Handbook to Dante* (Ginn & Co.: Boston, 1887).
Schneider, Friedrich, *Dante* (Böhlaus: Weimar, 1951).
Sedgwick, Henry Dwight, *Dante* (Yale University: New Haven, 1920).
Selfe, Rose, *How Dante Climbed the Mountain* (Cassell: London, 1888)
Shore, Arabella, *Dante* (Chapman & Hall: London, 1886).
Spoerri, T., *Einführung in die Göttliche Kömodie* (Speer: Zürich, 1946).
Symonds, John Addington, *Introduction to Dante* (Black: London, 1899).
Terrade, E.,*Etudes sur Dante* (Poussilgue: Paris, 1904).
Toynbee, Paget, *Britain's Tribute to Dante* (British Academy: London, 1921).
Toynbee, P., *Concise Dictionary of Dante* (Oxford: Clarendon, 1914/1916).
Toynbee, P., *Dante* (Methuen: London, 1905).
Toynbee, P., *Dante* (Methuen: London, 1910).
Toynbee, P., *Dante in English Literature* (Methuen: London, 1909).
Toynbee, P., *Dante Studies* (Methuen: London, 1902)
Toynbee, P., *In the footprints of Dante* (Methuen: London, 1907).
Tozer, H.F., *Dante: La Divina Commedia* (Oxford: Clarendon, 1902)
Tozer, H.F., *Notes on the Inferno* (Oxford: Clarendon, 1902)
Tozer, H.F., *Notes on the Purgatorio* (Oxford: Clarendon, 1902)
Traquair Phoebe, & J.S. Black, *Dante Illustrations* (privately printed: Edinburgh, 1890).
Vallone, Aldo, *Gli Studi Danteschi* (Olschki: Florence, 1950). 3 vols.
Vollone, A., *La Critica Dantesca Contemporanea* (Nistri-Lischi: Pisa, 1953).
Venturi, T. da Luigi, *Similitudini Dantesche* (Sansoni: Florence, 1911).
Vernon, W.W., *Readings in the Inferno* (Macmillan: London, 1894). 2 vols.
Vernon, W.W., *Readings in the Paradiso* (1900). 2 vols.
Vernon, W.W., E. *Readings in the Purgatorio* (Macmillan: London, 1889). 2 vols.
Vincent, E.R., *Re-reading the Divine Comedy* (British Academy: London, 1945).
Volkmann, L., *Iconografia Dantesca* (Breitkopf & Härtel: Leipzig, 1897).
Vossler, Karl, *Die göttliche komödie* (Winters: Heidelberg, 1907).
Whitfield J.H., *Dante and Virgil* (Blackwell: Oxford, 1949).
Whiting, Mary Bradford, *Dante and his poetry* (Harrap: London, 1932).
Whiting, M.B., *Dante: the man and the poet* (Heffer: Cambridge, 1922).
Wicksteed, P.H., *Dante* (Mathews: London, 1905).
Wicksteed P.H., & E.G. Gardner, *Dante & Giovanni del Virgilio* (Constable: London, 1902)
Williams, Charles, *The figure of Beatrice* (Faber: London, 1943).
Witte, Karl, *Essays on Dante* (Duckworth: London, 1898).

## BOOK REVIEWS

**The Historic Landscape of Loch Lomond and the Trossachs.** S D Boyle et al. Royal Commission on Ancient and Historic Monuments (RCAHMS) / Historic Scotland. 32 pp. 1 902419 20 0. £5.

Explores the past and present archaeology / landscape of Scotland's first National Park. Illustrated/mapped in full colour this is an authoritative high quality study. It draws extensively on the work of the Historic Landscape Assessment (HLA) project, with a timely discussion of cultural landscape management.

**The Historic Landscape of the Cairngorms** is a similar work for the second National Park, authored by David Cowley and S Gowan. 32pp. £5.

**'Well Sheltered and Watered': Menstrie Glen, a farming landscape near Stirling.** David Cowley and John G Harrison. RCAHMS. 71pp. 1 9012419 25 1. £5.

We described the coming of this oustanding work in volume 21 1998 pp 137-8 of this journal. A quality A4 book illustrated in full colour it is produced with some sponsorship by several local organisations, this FNH included. Editorial notes are followed by 4 pages on the source material; 14 on the farming history; 10 on settlements; 20 on the archaeology; and 3 of conclusions – particularly the influence of the unusual documentation collected and generated in the mid 18th century by John Wright, the laird of Loss.

**The Shielings and Drove Ways of Loch Lomondside.** John Mitchell. Stirling Libraries. 32pp 1 870542 43 6. £1.95.

A valuable illustrated study by a man of Drymen, a key village in droving times.

**In Search of Scotland.** Editor Gordon Menzies. Principle historical adviser T C Smout. Polygon/BBC Scotland/Historic Scotland. 250pp. 1 90293023 1. £12.99.

This is the companion book to the BBC tv series of the same name produced by Menzies and presented by Fiona Watson, with other leading historians – Armit, Woolf, Borrow, Lynch, Smout,Cowan, Whatley, Fraser,and Finlay. From the Stone Age to the present the ten chapters cover – Ancestors; Birth of a nation; Impact of the monk; The wars of independence; Court and kirk; The European lifeline; Union; Crucible of the modern world; The Victorian achievement; A century of pain and pleasure. Well pesented and illustrated including colour, it ends with some further reading, genealogy, notes on authors, and index.

# THE STIRLINGS OF KEIR IN THE 18TH CENTURY, RESTORING THE FAMILY FORTUNES IN THE BRITISH EMPIRE

Bill Inglis

Figure 1
James Stirling of Keir 1679-1749 m. 1704 Marion Stuart daughter of Lord Blantyre d. 1770

## Introduction

The papers of the Stirlings of Keir allow us to put a local focus on a number of relatively neglected themes in Scottish 18th century history.[1] While considerable research has been completed on the part played by the Scottish landed class in agrarian improvement in the late 18th century[2] much less is known about how these families managed their estates and finances in the late 17th and early 18th centuries. It is clear for example that the lowland landlords built new houses at this time and began to live more expensively[3] but the productivity of their estates does not appear to have increased markedly.[4] How did they manage to avoid bankruptcy? It has been argued that this predicament led them to exploit the new opportunities which the Union of 1707 made available to Scots in the British Empire with more enthusiasm than the English landowning class[5] but detailed descriptions of how particular families set about this are rare. Also little has been written about how these Scottish adventurers repatriated their capital from overseas and how far the money was used to fuel agricultural development from the middle of the 18th century.

## The Growing Financial Problems of the Stirlings of Keir in the late 17th and early 18th Centuries

By the standards of the early 18th century the Stirlings of Keir were an extremely wealthy family. In 1716 James Stirling of Keir forfeited his estate of Keir and Cawdor because of his involvement in the Jacobite rebellion of 1715. The returns taken in consequence by the commissioners for the forfeited estates allow us to assess the wealth of the family.[6] The total rental of the estate, which was partly in kind according to these returns was

*£628 sterling,[7] 308 bolls of bear, 426 of meall, 2 stones of cheese, 4 stones of butter, 19 geese, 16 wedders, 530 hens and 184 capons*

Using the monetary values of the crops and animals, which are mentioned in the returns the total cash value of the rental comes to £953/6/8.[8]

This sum is meaningless without a yardstick for comparison. Even though little is known about incomes in the early 18th century the annual pay of a labourer at this time has been estimated to between £8 and £10 sterling depending on the cost of oats, which varied between and within years.[9] Of course the income earned by a labourer at that time was very limited only enabling him to feed his family but it does show the wealth of the Stirlings of Keir in the early 18th century.

It was only during the last three decades of the 17th century that the Stirlings began to run into financial problems.

In the 1660s they were in a strong position. When Sir George Stirling died in June 1667, according to his inventory, he owed slightly over £80 net or 10 % of their annual rental, a very small sum given the value of the estate.[10]

From this point the decline was steep. By the death of Sir John Stirling in March 1684 the net debt had risen to £830,[11] by 1695-96 it was £2,083,[12] and in 1720 four years after the forfeiture it had shot up to £8,083.[13] With the interest rate on loans around 5 % at this time the annual sum paid in interest would have been close to £420 or nearly half the yearly rental on the estate. Not only did this sum cut into the income of the family, but it made any chance of paying off the principal extremely remote.

How had this happened? It is likely that the main cause was house building. The returns for the forfeited estates report that the Stirlings had two good quality country houses, one at Keir and the other at Cawdor, and that a new house was being built at Keir, which was incomplete in 1716.[14] So the Stirlings, like many other landed families in Lowland Scotland, had moved out of their castles and built country houses in the later 17th century.[15] In the case of Keir a date for the building of the first country house can be hazarded. In his will dated March 1 1664 Sir George mentions some virginells *"in the laigh tour in the Keir"* implying that the tower house was still being used at the time.[16] This would place the building of the first country house after that date, which coincides with the sudden rise in the family debts.

But the problems were to increase. Since James Stirling had forfeited the estate in 1716 it was bought back by a group of the Stirling relatives led by Lord Blantyre, James brother in law, in 1724 for £14,149 on the understanding that John Stirling, James eldest son, would take over from his father.[17] There is no record indicating whether the Stirlings paid this money back to the purchasers. All that exists are John's accounts on taking over the estate between 1729 and 1731 and in them he identifies £6,541 as owed to the purchasers of the estate, which considerably increased the overall debt.[18]

The situation John faced, on taking over the estate, was therefore very serious. The debt had risen to £14,937, which was over half the value of the estate that John estimated in 1731 was worth just over £29,000. John had also to provide an income for his mother and father as suited their status. The only encouraging sign was that the rental from the estate had risen considerably since 1716 whether from better management or increased prosperity is not clear. John's account makes it possible to provide an estimate of his financial position in 1731 as follows[19]

Rental from the estate - - - - - - - - - - - - - - - - - - - - - - - - - - - - - £1,427/5/7[20]
Deduct interest on the debt assuming a rate of 5% - - - - - - - - - - - £818/0/0
annual income paid to his father - - - - - - - - - - - - - - - - - - - - - £300/0/0
Total Deductions - - - - - - - - - - - - - - - - - - - - - - - - - - - - - £1118/0/0
Income left to John Stirling of Keir - - - - - - - - - - - - - - - - - - - £309/5/7

Despite being in overall charge of the estate John was therefore in a very difficult position. The rental of the estate was heavily encumbered with payments on the debt and to his parents leaving him with an income that was only 20 % of the rental. Out of this he had to maintain two houses and live to the standard of a laird. A letter written by Henry, his brother, from India on January 23 1740 illustrates the severity of the situation. In the letter Henry recalls his last conversation with John before leaving for India three years earlier in which John had emphasised how serious was the financial position of the estate. To illustrate this John had described himself as only *"the factor of the estate for the family"*[21]

If John's situation was bad that of the other children was far worse.[22] At the time when John took over the estate James and Marion Stirling had eight sons and six daughters in addition to John, who had survived out of the 22 children born to them. Clearly there was no possibility of providing for them on a generous scale. In fact it was difficult to see how anything could be given to them at all.

James Stirling and his son John devised a settlement, which saved face but did little to provide support for the children. They agreed that each of the sons should receive £333 but only after both their father and mother had died ie when the estate did not have to provide for the parents. This arrangement was little use to the sons since both parents were very healthy, James dying in 1749 and Marion in 1770. One son, the second eldest, Archibald, was an exception since John's accounts show that he received his £333 from his father James and from John in 1733 but there is no record of any of the other sons being given anything more than small change. The daughters were to be treated in a similar manner. They were to receive an annuity of £33 while unmarried and £333 as a dowry on marriage but again these provisions were only to operate when both parents had died.[23]

What careers then were open to James Stirling's sons? The conventional avenues of the army and the church were closed. Both would have cost money. No career in the army was possible without money since ranks of Major and above had to be purchased. The church also was closed since it required an expensive education even if James Stirling had not been a fervent Episcopalian and an opponent of the Established Church in Scotland. Even a modest apprenticeship to a lawyer or merchant or to a high status artisan like a jeweller, which were favoured careers for younger sons of the gentry, was out of the question.[24] Each son would have had to be provided with the same opportunity making it far too costly.

There only remained one possibility – trade, which did not require an apprenticeship. It was open to anybody with a sound basic education, which included accounting. An advantage would be some capital with which to get started – the lack of it was the problem, which exercised the Stirlings and as will be seen below which they overcame.

It is likely that many other landed families in Lowland Scotland experienced similar problems to the Stirlings. From 1660 the building of country houses to replace tower houses was widespread. With this trend went a more expensive lifestyle and as a result a higher level of debt.[25] At least two of the neighbours of the Stirlings had serious financial problems during the 18th century. By 1740 the Stirlings of Kippendavie were heavily in debt and had to be helped out by the Stirlings of Keir[26] who were beginning to turn the corner at that time while the Pearsons of Kippenross had to sell up their estate in 1772 because of injudicious house building.[27] In addition a considerable number of estates in Lowland Scotland were confiscated after the rebellion of 1715 which, as in the case of the Stirlings, will have led to increased financial difficulties for the families concerned. So the experience of the Stirlings of Keir may have been fairly typical.

**Launching the Stirling's Younger Sons, Archibald and Henry, in India**

Figure 2 Archibald Stirling of Keir 1710-1783

Archibald, the second eldest son of James Stirling, was born in 1710. As has already been indicated he was treated more generously than his other brothers being given £333 in 1733 long before the death of either of his parents. It is likely that this was because he and two of his younger brothers, Robert and James, were going out to Jamaica in that year to survey the prospects on the island and Archibald as the oldest brother of the three was given funds to see what could be established. He took goods to sell in Jamaica. It was not a very successful venture as far as Archibald was concerned because he found it difficult to sell the goods and consequently he returned to London late in 1734 leaving his two brothers on the island with virtually all his money exhausted.[28]

During the course of the next twelve months he decided to make his career in Bengal. India had only been opened to the Scots as a result of the Union of 1707 and very few of them had gone to India where the trade was controlled by the East India Company. It is clear from Archibald's behaviour that he was exploring the possibility of a career in India without any patronage either in London or in India.

Nor was any help available from the estate. In a letter dated December 9 1735 from London Archibald regrets that his brother John is unable to lend him any money to get him started in India. He makes no mention of the money he had already received in 1733. In the same letter Archibald lays out his scheme for establishing himself in India. Apparently by chance he had met a Captain Manley whose ship the Halifax was due to sail for India at the end of December 1735. He describes the plan that resulted from the meeting as follows

*"I have agreed with one Captain Manley to go his purser ------ I have paid him £60 for the berth which is reckoned very cheap and as the station I go in intitles me to the liberty of carrying a little cargo I have taken (borrowed) £300 to be paid at Bengall"*[29]

So Archibald's scheme was to go out to India as a purser, that is in charge of the ship's accounts. Presumably this was the only post on a ship which somebody with no naval qualifications could hold. Despite occupying this position he had to pay £60 for the passage. But in return he could take cargo, to the value of £300 which he would sell at a profit in Bengal. Archibald had therefore to borrow at least £410.

Archibald succeeded in raising two loans. First he borrowed £300 from a Mr. Fullerton just returned from India with a considerable fortune, who wanted to transfer money to Bengal. Archibald was to repay the loan in Bengal with 18% interest six months later. So Archibald had to sign a bond for £350 to Mr. Fullerton.[30] Since Archibald could offer no satisfactory security for such a sum his cousin James Stirling, the well-known mathematician and nicknamed "the Venetian" by the family, who was in London at the time guaranteed to pay the sum in case of default. A further £60 sterling was borrowed from Mr.Auchterlony, a Scots merchant in London. Archibald expected to pay him back from the proceeds of the goods he had taken to Jamaica which were gradually being sold by his brother Robert.

James Stirling, Archibald's cousin, who had acted as surety for both loans promptly sent a letter to John Stirling of Keir dated December 12 1735. In it he describes the debt and others he has incurred for John's family and in return asks John for a bond to cover him financially in case of disaster.[31] This request is reinforced by Archibald's letter of December 9 1735 and by letters they both sent to Archibald's father, James, during the course of the month.[32]

Both Archibald and his cousin James Stirling were of course being disingenuous. Neither wrote to John Stirling to ask if he was willing to provide the ultimate security for £410 sterling, which was nearly a third of the rental of the estate. He was told after the event. Archibald clearly felt very guilty about this manoeuvre because he claims in his letter of December 9 to John that he did not have time to write

*"--- it was not in my power to do it : the Captain being very much out of order I have been obliged to transact all his affairs with the Company* (the East India Company) *which has kept me in a perpetual confusion these ten days past so that it was not really in my power to write you"*

It is likely also that the following effusion from Archibald in the same letter springs from his guilty conscience

*"as for my part I do assure you that if it happens I should make a fortune, which I don't in the least doubt off, for there shall be neither industry nor application wanting I shall always be ready to assist the rest of my brothers to the utmost of my power as long as they follow those principles which men of virtue and honour ought : these are my present sentiments which I hope I will never alter."*[33]

Some comment is needed at this stage. Archibald had launched himself on a career in India without being given any money from the estate or borrowing from it. But the estate was still important as the ultimate surety for the loans, which he incurred, so such a venture was not open to many Scots at that time. On a less serious note the Stirling correspondence does not reveal what goods Archibald took out to Bengal. They would have been articles that Europeans would be prepared to buy. Such was the case twenty years later when Archibald's brother in law, David Esrkine, went out to India. One of the items, which he sold in Bombay, very successfully, was a consignment of earrings which proved very popular with the wives of the British sea captains living in the town.[34]

As if Archibald had not enough to do managing his own affairs he had plans as he said in his letter of December 9 1735 for " *disposing of Harry"*.

There was a real need for launching Henry as well, which is described by James Stirling the 'Venetian' in his letter of Christmas Day 1735 to Archibald's father James.

*"One great inconveniency attends all young people abroad which is if they have no relation on the spot it is hard for them to extend their credit as having nobody to prevent the embezzling of their effects and to see to their debts in case of death"*[35]

Death was all too common amongst Europeans going out east. It is starkly referred to in a comment made by Archibald about Harry's prospects in a letter of December 13 1735 to his father

*"All this I hope will agree with Harry for as he is young he cant fail of making his fortune **if he lives**."*[36](my emphasis)

The plans for Henry were all hatched by the resourceful Archibald and are described in his letter to John of December 9 1735

*"---I wrote you of a scheme I have of disposing of Harry, which was to get him out captain of the military to Bengal, a place of considerable profit and which will be*

*of great service to us both : ye way I propose of obtaining it was this. My Lord Wilmington has such an influence over the Company that they will do anything he desires them and I understand there is a particular friendship between him and Lord Cathcart who I dare say will serve my brother, —— so I think it is requisite that my father with Harry should wait on Lord Cathcart and that they should come up before the Parliament closes and get this thing done"* [37]

The plan is nothing if not audacious. Henry is only 17 and Archibald is proposing that he should command a company of sepoys (c 100 men) without any prior military training! The means to be used are also revealing. The Stirlings knew Lord Cathcart because he had an estate in Alloa. He was a rising politician with obvious influence but it is interesting that the Stirlings had no direct link to the East India Company which shows the limited Scottish influence at that time. Also once again a son is being launched without any money having to be provided by the estate.

There is also a hidden agenda. In a letter to John Stirling dated January 3 1736 cousin James the 'Venetian' who had helped Archibald so much indicates the real purpose of the scheme for Henry. He describes how Henry should prepare himself for his new appointment as follows

*"in the meantime he cannot spend his time better than in learning to write a good hand and book keeping by double entry if he goes in any military command he will have the knowledge of a free trade which is the principal thing"* [38]

So the real purpose of a post in the military in India was to trade.

A year later Henry went out as an officer with the East India Company though possibly only as a lieutenant.

### Archibald's and Henry's Careers in India

Archibald's career in India can be traced from letters sent home and from an account book, which he kept during his last year in India.

The first news of Archibald in India comes in a letter written by Henry to John Stirling dated February 6 1739 from India. He writes as follows

*"Baldy has had the good fortune to be the only man to escape the plague at Buparo? by which he has the management of all the Company's effects in that place."* [39]

Unfortunately it has not been possible to identify Buparo but this first news of Archibald reinforces the view that if you survived in India you were well on the way to making a fortune. In this instance Archibald as the sole survivor amongst the company officials at Buparo could monopolise the company trade for a time and thus make a considerable profit.

The first of Archibald's letters from India to have been preserved was written to John on October 25 1742 and it confirms that he is doing extremely well. He writes

*"As I'm upon money matters I shall beg leave to trouble you with a small sketch of*

*my own present situation and future views. I will continue in the Surat trade
and I shall sail in a few days for that port I have hitherto met with good success
both for myself and the owners which is the reason the employment has been so
constant and I hope will continue so until I have done my business. At present I
reckon myself worth £4,500 sterling and the voyage I am now going upon will I
expect improve my fortune a thousand or twelve hundred pounds. As soon as I
have laid up £8,000 I propose coming home"* [40]

Archibald's account of his financial situation is of considerable interest. Most
surprising is the money he has made from scratch in only five years and the
money he is likely to make quite soon. £8,000 sterling would have bought a
moderate estate in Scotland at the time. He has done exceptionally well to get
into the Surat trade. Surat, just north of Bombay was the main focus of trade
within India, also between India and Persia, and it was the first port where
European ships called as they reached India. The trade between Bengal and
Surat consisted of approximately 12 ships, by now in the hands of the
European traders. This little fleet went to Surat annually with raw materials,
like cotton and silk, and returned with the choicest luxury goods from Europe,
Persia and India which sold at a great profit in Calcutta. [41]

Archibald's one surviving account book from India started in February 1746
is revealing about his trade. He wisely spread his risks across a broad range of
goods, with a variety of traders and on a number of ships.

He traded in food, principally rice, sugar candy and fruit, for example
tamarinds, banyans and pears, as well as ghee (butter) and salt. Textiles were of
equal importance large quantities of cotton and silk being mentioned as are
cambrick and what he terms long cloth. Actual clothes did not play much part
in his stock, though handkerchiefs are mentioned and hickcloths which are
country clothes but whether they are Indian or European is not clear. Other
goods he sold were madeira wine and claret, silver, iron and battens, that is
timber flooring, and there is one mention of opium.

The general view is that Scots in the Empire traded by preference with their
own countrymen. This was not true of Archibald whose business associates
were of varied national and cultural backgrounds though of course there may
have been very few Scots in India at the time. The main European names
mentioned in his account book are English, two of whom Mr Jackson *"the
greatest trader we have"* and Daniel Lascelles, probably a partner, were especially
prominent. Also included are Indian merchants, especially Bodaporsal and
Mohanporsal with whom he does substantial trade, and Jewish merchants like
Moses Saloman and Joseph Fowke.

Archibald also spreads his risks among a number of ships. Names
mentioned include the Fort St.George and Fort St. David, the Queen of
Hungary, the Caesar and the Warwick. It is likely that he owned shares in some
of these ships. This number of ships shows that he was not only involved in
trade with Surat but also with the coastal commerce of the Bay of Bengal. [42]

In January 1747 Archibald sailed for Britain. By then he estimated his fortune at £23000 sterling and his main concern was the repatriation of the capital (see below.)[43]

Henry was much less successful than Archibald. His first letter home from India is dated February 6 1739. In it he complains that

*"Trade in this place is very small --- and all in the hands of oldstanders so I can expect to do little until I am advanced in the Company's service which cannot be for many years"* [44]

Henry was at Fort Marlborough, 100 miles south of Madras, which did not have the advantages of Madras or of Calcutta where Archibald was based and Henry, being very young, was not senior enough to get much trade. In the early 1740s things looked up when Archibald writes that Henry had

*"the title of Resident at Sillibar, a place which I believe you'll not find out in ye most modern maps for I dare say never christian was there before"* [45]

Again it has not been possible to identify Sillibar but Archibald writes that Henry was *"very well pleased"* and that he *"could pick up a good deal of money there"*. Nothing more is heard of Henry until John writes to Archibald in December 1747 stating that it will be a long time before Henry's estate can be settled.[46] Henry had clearly died some time before but there is no indication of the cause. He left approximately £1,000 sterling, much less than Archibald had made, but still a considerable sum considering that he had set out with nothing.[47]

### Establishing Robert and James Stirling in Jamaica

Jamaica was the most promising venue for ambitious young men in the early 18th century. Captured from the Spaniards in 1655 the island's potential for the production of sugar was quickly realised and a very lucrative trade between Jamaica and Britain was established by 1730.[48]

It is therefore not surprising that the first place which the young Stirlings, Archibald Robert and James, visited in their quest for a fortune was Kingston Jamaica in 1733 18 months before Archibald went to India. It was Archibald who first identified the main opportunities offered by the island to young men, becoming a trader or being *"bred a planter"*.[49]

Little account is given of the first option of going into trade. In 1734 Archibald certainly discounted the idea because his brothers had no capital. Yet Robert selected this option joining a trading company in Kingston where he either served an apprenticeship or was initially a clerk. Robert succeeded in this unlikely alternative partly through the impression he made on his contemporaries of all ages. Archibald hints at this in his letter of July 1734 from Jamaica to John Stirling in which he writes that

*"Roby has a good character with everybody in town* (Kingston)*"* while*"Jamy was unhappy at first"* [50]

Luck also seems to have played a part. On Christmas Day 1735 James Stirling, the 'Venetian', writing to James Stirling of Keir, Robert's father, describes how Mr Manning *"one of his* (Robert's) *Masters* who is an agent for the South Sea Company has

> *"got a place* (in the Company) *worth £4-5000 sterling in which case it is thought that he will give up his part in the house and either put Roby into it or some other considerable place under him*[51]

Frustratingly the letters do not indicate whether Robert benefited from Mr Manning's promotion but by 1742 he was clearly an independent trader because Archibald in a letter dated October 15 states that Robert is doing well as follows

> *"this war must be a fine harvest for Rob and I dare say he will make hay while the sun shines"* [52]

Robert had achieved this level only nine years after arriving in Jamaica. Quite why the war would benefit his trade is not clear unless the dominance of the British navy in the Atlantic and the Caribbean allowed British traders to monopolise the commerce of the area. Two letters later in the 1740s confirm Robert's status. The first from Archibald to John dated February 20 1746 states that Robert is in a trading partnership.[53] In the second on May 11 1748 which is written by Robert he complains that his partner Mr Ker is always ill and so he (Robert) has to do all the work.[54]

So Robert seems to have reached the top in a trading company without any initial capital despite Archibald's gloomy prognosis.

However everybody, including Robert, considered that training to be a planter was a much better route to success than trade for those with no initial resources. Robert gives a pithy description of how to progress in that career in his letter of June 9 1750 to Archibald from Kingston Jamaica. Archibald had written to ask him if it would be possible to establish Patrick Stirling of Kippendavie in Jamaica. As was mentioned above the Stirlings of Keir had to help out the Stirlings of Kippendavie in the 1740s because they were so heavily in debt. So bad was the situation that their eldest son could not afford to live on his estate when his father died and had to be launched in the world on a separate career without the advantage of capital. Robert describes the early stages of the career in planting as follows

> *"A young man that goes into that way of life must expect to go through a good deal of drudgery work at first. He will be about two years or 18 months at least before he can be presumed to be well enough acquainted with the business to take upon him the charge of a plantation as an overseer in which time he lives on the estate under the character of a bookkeeper to it, altho' that is the least part of the business he has to do, which is cheifly to take care of the stores and receive in and deliver out everything belonging to the plantation and to attend the negroes in the field and in other branches of their work relating to the making of sugar, in order to instruct him thoroughly in that art, and he has generally about £20 or*

*£25 per annum wages besides such fare as the plantation affords which in some places I assure you is not amiss and when he is deemed sufficiently qualified to be an overseer his friends get him into the first vacant berth of that kind, they hear of, where the salary is from £80 to £100, £150 and some £200 according to the size of the plantation and generosity of the employer or master. They have other opportunities of making money besides, such as buying negroes and bringing them up to trades.*[55]

Figure 3
Cane Cutting on a Jamaican Plantation in the 18th Century from a Contemporary Print

There is no doubt that the early stages of becoming a planter were as Robert says *"drudgery"*. He passes quickly over the supervision of the slaves in the field, which must have been a shock for young men straight from Scotland. They worked in the fields from dawn to dusk, planting, weeding and cutting cane depending on the season of the year in a climate that is very unsuited to hard labour since the average temperature is 30 centigrade and the atmosphere is very humid. It was even worse in the heat of the boiler house in which the cane was processed into sugar and rum in the first six months of the year. Inevitably the slaves were unwilling workers and the only way such a regime could be maintained was by frequent use of the lash.[56]

It is of course difficult for us to judge reactions at the time. The letters quoted in this paper were written before Wilberforce began his campaign for the abolition of the slave trade. There are no comments in them about attitudes to slavery in Jamaica or in Scotland, but the life of a bookkeeper was clearly harsh, if not brutalising, and the pay of £20 or £25 was not very generous.

When Robert estimates that a man need only be a bookkeeper for 18 months to two years he is being optimistic. There were probably 10 bookkeepers to every overseer and as Robert says promotion depends on having *"friends"*.

The job of the overseer was also difficult. Many owners were absentees and the overseer was responsible for the whole operation of the plantation which was far more than just planting and harvesting since the production of sugar and rum on a plantation was a demanding industrial process. In addition the overseer had to get the crop to port, negotiate its transport to Britain and ensure that appropriate supplies were ordered.

Robert mentions that an overseer can buy his own slaves, teach them trades and sell them at a profit. This was only one way of amassing capital which if successful could lead to achieving the ultimate aim of every young man starting out in Jamaica which was to own a plantation.

### Robert and James Careers in Jamaica

Since Robert and James careers in Jamaica eventually interlocked they will be described together. As has already been indicated Robert succeeded in becoming a partner in a trading company in Kingston. Occasionally Robert refers to James in his letters to Archibald and it is obvious that James became a planter following the path outlined by Robert above.

Though Robert succeeded in becoming a partner he clearly did not make the same sort of fortune as Archibald did in India. Trade was erratic. Already the paradox of Robert's trade being good in time of war has been pointed out and the reverse appears to have been the case namely that trade stagnated in times of peace. In a letter dated July 1 1749 Robert writes

*"The peace has made an almost perfect stagnation in trade"* [57]

Robert's company encountered other serious problems. One of their main activities was to import goods from London to Jamaica and they found it difficult to buy cargoes in London without an agent who could guarantee payment.[58] When Robert eventually wound up his trading business he writes in a letter to Archibald dated March 12 1750 that

*"I have two partnerships to make up and some lawsuits to finish"* [59]

At least one of these lawsuits was in London.

It is not surprising then that a couple of years earlier in 1748 Robert had taken the plunge and purchased a plantation. Probably Archibald's success in India spurred him on and the chance of borrowing money from Archibald was an obvious incentive. At first all seemed to be going well. In a letter to John dated March 1748 he writes triumphantly

*"I have lately made a purchase of an estate here which stands me very  nearly £8000 sterling so that you can imagine I have occasion for the  assistance of all my friends to help me in paying the purchase money. I have indeed met with some very good ones by whose means the purchase has come pretty easy to me."* [60]

Optimistically he estimates that after more slaves have been bought the estate will yield annually 120 hogsheads of sugar and 40 to 50 puncheons of rum, giving him a profit of £2,000 annually which will allow him to return home in four or five years time with his debts paid.

It was not to be. Already in a letter of July 1 1749 faced with having to borrow more money from Archibald and his elder brother's insistence on hearing the true state of his business Robert admits that he has difficulties. He acknowledges that weather can hit the yield of an estate badly. He writes

*"a plantation is liable to many accidents such as dry weather which stunts the canes and strong winds that often lodge them by which our crops fall short."*

He has also borrowed heavily to purchase the estate. He owes a Mr Morse in Jamaica close on £2,500 and his debt to Archibald has risen to £1,500, not to mention the generous friends mentioned above.[61] Finally the output even in a good year never seems to have reached anywhere near Robert's early estimates.[62]

Despite these problems he decided in partnership with his brother James to buy another plantation Hampden in the North of Jamaica near Montego Bay in the autumn of 1753 for £9,000. Robert describes this as a *"bold push"* and it involved borrowing more money, this time from John, taking the money owed to Archibald and John to £2,500, a considerable sum.[63]

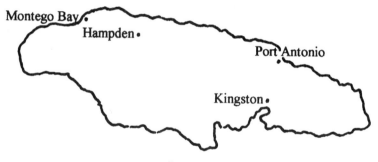

Figure 4
Jamaica in the 18th Century showing Hampden Robert Stirling's main Plantation

The next two years appear to have gone quite well. During this period Robert acquired a government appointment in Jamaica as Receiver General. He shared the proceeds with Robert Graham, a nephew of Graham of Gartmore, who held the patent for the post. The income he gained from this appointment is not clear but it was obviously profitable.[64] Possibly as a result of being in this post Robert went to Havana in April 1755 to negotiate compensation from the Spanish authorities for loss of cargoes during the recent war. He returned to Jamaica with a significant proportion of the compensation paid. Such was his success that when James became unwell in summer 1755 he was able to buy him out from all his Jamaican interests. James was to return to Scotland and during his lifetime Robert undertook to pay him an annual income of £300 .[65]

But from this point on Robert's fortunes declined. In his last surviving letter in the Stirling collection from his plantation of Hampden dated 23 July 1757 it is clear that his debts are still considerable since he dare not return home because of the actions which are likely to be taken against him by his creditors.[66] It is left to Archibald to describe the deteriorating situation with his brother in a letter to him from Keir dated March 31 1763

> *"Yours of January 14 came to hand the 13th instant which is the only one you have favoured me with now for upwards of three years and it is going on to six since you remitted me a farthing————how can you imagine I can afford to let such a sum in a manner lye dead in your hands."* [67]

It is clear that Robert was not attempting to pay interest on his debt to Archibald, which by this time had risen to the large sum of £5757 sterling.

At the same time to Archibald's amazement Robert acquired yet another plantation which leads Archibald to make the following comments in a letter of November 18 1763

> *"I have been conversing with some Jamaica folks concerning your late purchase and their opinion seems to be that in a young man beginning in the world with a good stock it would have been a rational step, but in your time of life and so immersed in debt, it was most inconsiderate with regard to yourself and not a little unjust with regard to your creditors as you are rendered less able than ever (at least for some years) to do justice to them, however the proof of the pudding is in the eating of it, so shall say no more on this disagreeable subject."* [68]

Robert died in the following year, 1764. While he owned three plantations, which the family could eventually inherit, since Robert had no legitimate descendants, he still left debts of above £40,000 sterling.[69] So much had to be done by Archibald to ensure that the Jamaican venture of Robert and James would be a success.

### Repatriating the Capital from India and Jamaica and its Impact on the Family's Fortunes

As has already been indicated above Archibald reckoned in 1747 that he had made a fortune of £23,000 sterling

Repatriating this amount of money from India to Britain was difficult. In Britain it was possible to transfer funds from London to other provincial towns through the embryonic banking and credit system but no such facilities existed between India and Britain when Archibald returned home. So most men in his position repatriated their money through goods. Archibald used one of the most popular methods of the time, also employed by Clive of India.[70] He bought diamonds in Madras and sent them home by boat to be sold at a profit by an agent in London. Archibald's correspondence with John reveals that he transferred close on £7,000 by this method on three ships in the year before he came home.[71] A second way of repatriating capital was the more conventional approach of transporting luxuries from India that could be sold in Britain, for example silk, which is probably how Archibald repatriated most of his capital.

It is difficult to determine how much capital was returned home. By the time Archibald arrived in London in November 1748 he had £10,000 back in Britain, £2,200 lent to John and the rest invested in Government funds.[72] But much more was expected. After his arrival Archibald stayed in London for six months despite his father being extremely ill and eventually dying.[73] The reason for this apparent callousness is that he was expecting ships from India with his goods on board, which would have to be sold in London. John assured him that everybody in the family accepted that it was essential for him to stay in London to ensure that he got what was due to him.[74]

Unfortunately there is no record in the Stirling letters of the sum, which Archibald eventually brought home but a reasonable estimate can be made because within six months of his return he had bought the estate of Cawdor from his brother John. According to John Cawdor was worth £12,281 in 1731.[75] By the 1740s when Archibald made the purchase its rents appear on average to have risen 25 % giving the estate a value of approximately £15,500.[76] It is likely that Archibald paid the full market price. Throughout their dealings with each other, for example lending money to each other, the brothers expected to pay the going rate of interest and they will have applied the same principles to the purchase of an estate.[77] In addition according to a letter written by Robert in July 1749 Archibald was thinking of rebuilding the house at Cawdor.[78] He will also have put money aside for improving the estate, which was becoming the fashion at that time, and he was able to lend Robert £1,500 so it is likely that he had repatriated at least £25,000.

At this point it is important to note that John held the Keir estate until his death in 1757. He never married possibly because of the financial problems of the estate. So when he died it came to Archibald as the next in line.

As will already be evident from Robert's financial problems repatriating capital from Jamaica was far more difficult than from India. In fact far from Robert's efforts leading to the transfer of capital to Scotland the reverse was the case with Archibald, as is pointed out above, having to support his brother with sizeable loans which totalled £5,757 by the time Robert died in 1764.

For some time Archibald despaired of being able to rescue anything from Jamaica. Robert's debts were over £40,000 against three estates that were in the circumstances difficult to sell. At one point Patrick Stirling of Kippendavie who was now running the plantations in Jamaica recommended that Archibald borrow in order to relieve the plantations of debt and Archibald describes what to him was a nightmare possibility in his letter of November 19 1769

> "had I followed your advice and borrowed the further sum of £12,000 to relieve the Jamaican estates I shou'd in all probability have died leaving £20,000 sterling locked up there and my own estate (in Scotland) so burthened with debt as must —————in the end have concerned the estate itself which wou'd have been letting go the substance and biting at the shadows."[79]

In the end Archibald hit upon an effective strategy. He and his brother James bought the principal of the three estates owned by Robert and sold one of them.[80] As a result cash was raised to pay off most of the creditors, which was achieved by 1777.

The success of this strategy is shown in Archibald's annual assessment of his own financial state, which he completed every January 1st. In 1778 he was able to report for the first time a net gain from selling the crops of the Jamaican estates in Britain of £1,700 for that year.[81] Each subsequent year until Archibald's death in 1783 he was able to report a profit from the sale of sugar and rum in Britain which totalled over £22,000 out of which the cost of sending some supplies to Jamaica each year had to be deducted. So it is likely that Archibald repatriated approximately £20,000 from Jamaica to Scotland.[82] To this sum must be added the £300 annuity which James enjoyed in 12 years living in Scotland totalling £3,600. Thus the Stirlings transferred just short of £25,000 from Jamaica to Scotland between 1755 and 1783. At the same time with the death of his brother James in 1777, again without descendants, Archibald could count the value of two plantations amongst his assets even though one of them still owed significant debts.

It is clearly difficult to arrive at precise sums but it is likely that the Stirling family principally through the efforts of Archibald repatriated over £50,000 sterling in capital to Scotland in these years. It is interesting that this sum is approximately 160 % of the value of the estate in 1731 – a considerable achievement.

It remains to sum up the impact of the activities of the sons of James Stirling on the estate between 1731 and 1783. It will be recalled that when John Stirling took over the estate in 1729-31 its net value when the debts owed by the family had been deducted was just over £14,000. On January 1st 1783 the year he died Archibald estimated that his net assets including the two estates, plantations etc were £116,749, over eight times the value in 1729-31.[83]

The composition of this last sum is interesting. The estate of Keir and Cawdor was worth £88,000 and their plantations were valued at £37,500, totalling £125,500. The estate was still carrying a net debt of just over £10,000. It is interesting that the major asset of the family was still the estate of Keir and Cawdor, which had risen in value from just over £29,000 in 1729 to £88,000 in 1783.

The capital earned in India and Jamaica was the main reason for the increased value of the estate of Keir and Cawdor in 1783. Some of it clearly was used to buy more land. For example Arnhall was bought from the Duke of Atholl in 1764 for £5,000.[84] But a much greater sum went to exploiting all the opportunities presented by the Agricultural Revolution, which was gathering pace from the middle of the 18th century. For the years 1760 to 1781 Archibald records his annual expenditure on agricultural improvements which came to just over £13,000 in total.[85] Since he left no similar record for the 1750s it is likely that in all he could have spent over £20,000 in this way. Estates were being improved initially through surveys, then by enclosure, followed by resting the land, dyking, draining, building new farms and outhouses and restocking. These changes were expensive and as a consequence had to be completed piecemeal over decades and required large inputs of capital.[86] It is interesting that while many landowners found it difficult to continue spending on their estates in the early 1770s because of poor harvests the Stirlings even increased their investment at that time.[87] The money, which the Stirlings earned in Jamaica and in India came just at the right time to exploit the changes in farming which were taking place over this period.

What did the Stirlings do with the remainder of the money earned in the Empire? It is likely that most of it went to finance an improved life style. Certainly between 1761 and 1781 nearly £5,000 was spent on buildings at Keir and Cawdor and almost £3,000 on furniture but only a careful survey of all their account books at this time will determine how all the money was spent.

At the beginning of this paper it was pointed out that the problems faced by the Stirlings of Keir were similar to those encountered by many other landed families in Scotland in the early 18th century. It is likely that with varying degrees of success they also exploited the opportunities offered by the British Empire after it was opened to the Scots as a result of the Union. The capital, which they earned, like the Stirlings, will have been repatriated and fed into their estates at a crucial time in the economic development of Scotland.

## Acknowledgements

I would like to thank George Dixon for the great help he has given me with this paper especially in relation to the sources. Of course any errors are entirely my own.

The portraits of the Stirling family are taken from Sir William Fraser's – *The Stirlings of Keir and their Family Papers* published privately Edinburgh 1858

## References

[1] Glasgow City Archives T-SK
[2] Devine, T. M. *The Transformation of Rural Scotland : Social Change and the Agrarian Economy 1660-1815* Edinburgh University Press, Edinburgh 1994
[3] Whatley C.A. *Scottish Society 1707-1830* Manchester University Press, Manchester 2000 pp.26-28.
[4] Ibid. pp.32-33
[5] Colley L. *Britons, Forging the Nation 1707-1837* Pimlico Press, London 1992 pp.128-129.
[6] National Archives of Scotland Forfeited Estates E 637/1 Nov. 8 1716.
[7] The preferred currency in the family papers of the Stirlings in the early 18th century was the Scots pound shifting to sterling later in the century. For clarity however all sums will be quoted in sterling in the main text of this paper.
[8] Two estates were confiscated in Dunblane, Keir and Cromlix. The monetary equivalents for the items in kind quoted in the returns for the two estates NAS E 623/1 and 637/1 are as follows in Scots (a Scots pound is 1/12 of a pound sterling) £5 each for a boll of meal or bear, £1/6/8 for a stone of cheese, £2/13/4 for a stone of butter, 13/4 for a goose, £3/6/8 for a wedder, 6/8 for a capon and 4/- each for a hen.

[9] Inglis B. (1999)'Wealth, poverty and status in Dunblane 300 years ago' *Scottish Local History* Vol. 46, pp7-14.

[10] N.A.S. Dunblane Commissary Court, Register of Testaments, Sir George Stirling of Keir, CC6/5/17 p. 79.

[11] N.A.S. D.C.C. Register of Testaments, Sir John Stirling of Keir, CC6/5/20 conf. November 8 1688.

[12] G.C.A. Charge and Discharge James Robertson of his Intromissions with Keir's Rents 1695 T-SK 21 Box 1.

[13] G.C.A. A Particular List of the Haile Bonds Granted by the Purchasers of the Estate of Keir 1720 T-SK 21 Box 1.

[14] N.A.S. Forfeited Estates E 637/1.

[15] Whatley C.A. *Scottish Society 1707-1830* Manchester University Press, Manchester 2000 pp26-28.

[16] N.A.S. D.C.C. Register of Testaments, Sir George Stirling of Keir CC6/5/17 p.79.

[17] G.C.A. T-SK 1/46.

[18] G.C.A. John Stirling of Keir, Memorandum of Various Financial Transactions 1728-41 T-SK 14/1

[19] Ibid.

[20] This is John Stirling's estimate of the rental after payment of teinds and taxes.

[21] G.C.A. Stirlings of Keir, Henry Stirling to John Stirling of Keir, January 29 1740, T-SK 11/2/23

[22] G.C.A. John Stirling of Keir Memorandum T-SK 14/1

[23] Ibid.

[24] Houston R.A. *Social Change in the Age of Enlightenment* Clarendon Press, Oxford 1994 p.84.

[25] Whatley C.A. *Scottish Society 1707-1830* Manchester University Press, Manchester p.27.

[26] G.C.A. Declaration Patrick Stirling of Kippendavie to John Stirling of Keir February 20 1744 T-SK 1/51/16.

[27] G.C.A. Archibald Stirling of Keir's Letter Book 1763-1776, Archibald to Patrick Stirling of Kippendavie T-SK 15/11 P.39-40.

[28] G.C.A. Archibald Stirling to John Stirling of Keir July 1734, T-SK 11/2/15

[29] G.C.A. Archibald to John, December 9 1735, T-SK 11/2/17

[30] Ibid.

[31] G.C.A. James Stirling the 'Venetian' to John Stirling, December 12 1735, T-SK 11/2/18.

[32] G.C.A. Archibald to his father James Stirling of Keir, December 13 1735, T-SK 11/2/19 and James Stirling the 'Venetian' to the same T-SK 11/2/20

[33] G.C.A. Archibald to John, December 9 1735, T-SK 11/2/17.

[34] G.C.A. David Erskine to Archibald, T-SK 11/2/70.

[35] G.C.A. James Stirling the 'Venetian' to James Stirling of Keir, December 25 1735, T-SK 11/2/20

[36] G.C.A. Archibald to his father James Stirling of Keir, December 13 1735 T-SK 11/2/19.

[37] G.C.A. Archibald to John, December 9 1735, T-SK 11/2/17

[38] G.C.A. James Stirling the 'Venetian' to John, January 3 1736, T-SK 11/2/16.

[39] G.C.A. Henry to John, February 6 1739, T-SK 11/2/22.

[40] G.C.A. Archibald to John, October 25 1742, T-SK 11/2/24.

[41] Marshall P.J. *East Indian Fortunes* Oxford University Press, London 1976 pp.77-79.

[42] G.C.A. Archibald Stirling of Keir Account Book 1747-54, T-SK 15/1

[43] G.C.A. Archibald to John, February 4 1748, T-SK 11/2/37.

[44] G.C.A. Henry to John, February 6 1739, T-SK 11/2/22.

[45] G.C.A. Archibald to John, October 25 1742, T-SK 11/2/24.

[46] G.C.A. John to Archibald, November 1 1748, T-SK 11/2/46.

[47] G.C.A. Archibald to John, December 13 1748, T-SK 11/2/51.
[48] Craton M. & Walvin J. *A Jamaican Plantation, The History of Worthy Park 1670-1970*, University of Toronto Press, Toronto 1970 p.52.
[49] G.C.A. Archibald to John, July 1734, T-SK 11/2/18.
[50] Ibid.
[51] G.C.A James Stirling the 'Venetian' to James Stirling of Keir December 25 1735 T-SK 11/2/20.
[52] G.C.A. Archibald to John, October 25 1742, T-SK 11/2/24.
[53] G.C.A. Archibald to John, February 20 1746, T-SK 11/2/32.
[54] G.C.A. Robert Stirling to Archibald, May 11 1748, T-SK 11/2/41.
[55] G.C.A. Robert to John, June 9 1750, T-SK 11/2/69.
[56] Craton M. & Walvin J. *A Jamaican Plantation, The History of Worthy Park 1690-1970*, Toronto University Press, Toronto p.125.
[57] G.C.A. Robert to Archibald, July 1 1749, T-SK 11/2/64.
[58] G.C.A. Robert to Archibald, May 11 1748, T-SK 11/2/41.
[59] G.C.A. Robert to Archibald, March 12 1750, T-SK 11/2/68.
[60] G.C.A. Robert to John, March 1748, T-SK 11/2/38.
[61] G.C.A. Robert to Archibald, July 1 1749, T-SK 11/2/64.
[62] G.C.A. Robert to Archibald, September 30 1753, T-SK 11/2/81.
[63] Ibid.
[64] G.C.A. Robert to Archibald, July 24 & September 5 1754, T-SK 11/2/83 & 84.
[65] G.C.A. Robert to Archibald, April 17 1755, T-SK 11/2/85.
[66] G.C.A. Robert to Archibald, July 23 1757, T-SK 11/2/95.
[67] G.C.A. Stirling of Keir, Archibald to Robert, March 31 1763, Archibald Stirling of Keir Letter Book 1763-1776 T-SK 15/11 p.1.
[68] G.C.A. Archibald to Robert, November 18 1763, Archibald Stirling's Letter Book T-SK 15/11 p. 2.
[69] G.C.A. Archibald to Patrick Stirling of Kippendavie, November 19 1769, Archibald Stirling of Keir's Letter Book T-SK 15/11 p.19-20.
[70] Marshall P.J. *East India Fortunes*, Oxford University Press, London 1976 p.221.
[71] G.C.A. Archibald to John, December 9 1745, November 30 1746, and February 20 1747 T-SK 11/2/27,29 & 32.
[72] G.C.A. Archibald to John, November 22 1748, T-SK 11/2/49.
[73] G.C.A. Archibald to John, February 2 1749, T-SK 11/2/54.
[74] G.C.A. John to Archibald, February 10 1749, T-SK 11/2/55.
[75] G.C.A. John Stirling of Keir. Memorandum T-SK 14/1.
[76] G.C.A. Cf. Rentals of Cadder, T-SK 20/1 & 20/75.
[77] G.C.A. Archibald to John, February 4 1747, T-SK 11/2/37.
[78] G.C.A. Robert to Archibald, June 9 1750, T-SK 11/2/69.
[79] G.C.A. Archibald to Patrick Stirling of Kippendavie, Letter Book T-SK 15/11 p.19-20.
[80] G.C.A. eg Archibald to James Stirling, January 18 1770, Letter Book, T-SK 15/11 p.23.
[81] G.C.A. Archibald Stirling, Annual States of Affairs, January 1 1778 T-SK 15/7.
[82] Ibid.
[83] Ibid.
[84] G.C.A. Archibald Stirling of Keir, Letter Book, Archibald to John Mackenzie, August 4 1765, T-SK 15/11 p. 8.
[85] G.C.A. Archibald Stirling States of Expenditure (on building, charity, improvements) 1761-81 T-SK 15/5.
[86] Devine T.M. *Transformation of Rural Scotland : Social Change and the Agrarian Economy 1660-1815* Edinburgh University Press, Edinburgh 1994 pp 101-102.
[87] Ibid. p.74.

## BOOK REVIEWS

**Scotland a History: 8000BC-AD2000.** Fiona Watson. Tempus Publishing. 220pp. 0 7524 1796 7. £11.99

A fresh perspective, coinciding with the BBC tv series 'In Search of Scotland' for which she is the presenter, and also fronts the BBC radio 'History File', it is set out in 10 lively well illustrated chapters – Land, waters, sky; Settlers and invaders 8000-2500BC; Land and community 2500-80BC; Amalgamation 80-800; Consolidation and assimilation 800-1286; Scotland united? 1286-1357; Scotland revealed 1357-1542; Reformation and revolution 1542-1742; Scotland in Britain 1702-1850; Scotland renewed 1850-2000. These are followed with Further reading; Maps of 1. zones of early peoples, 2. towns and regions; then Genealogies – 1. Scottish succession 843-1097, 2. 1034-1371, 3. JamesVI's to the English throne.

**The Battle of Bannockburn, 1314.** Aryeh Nusbacher. Tempus. 160pp. 0 7524 1783 5. Hbk £19.99.

Somewhat infornally and racilly, the military background author takes us through the personalities, politics, actions of the midsummer battle. His aim is to attempt to describe as factually as possible events of the day based on – the little existing primary source material, the controversial second hand accounts and inferences one can make, the authorities consultable, the legends, the ground places, the realities of the time – treason, loyalties, chivalry. It will always be an impressive, controversial story. This author adds some interesting views to the story, including the likelihood reliance of many Scottish nobles on their English estates; and the Church's relationship to the Pope and France, not to England.

**On the Trail of Bonnie Prince Charlie.** David Ross. Luath Press. 130pp. 0 946487 68 5. £7.99.

This biker popular history trail blazer of Wallace and of The Bruce, takes us in lively detail with maps and illustrations in the steps of the Young Pretender's Jacobite '45 Uprising campaign to retake the throne of Scotland. The hard won successes southwards, the turning point of Derby, sadly back to the disastrous Culloden, then the amazing five months on the run till the embarking on the L' Hereuse for France.

**The Kings and Queens of Scotland.** Richard Oram editor. Tempus. 256pp. 0 7524 1991 9. £14.99.

This is an authoritative history, from the earliest Scots and Pictish kings through the Union of the Crowns. Presented in five chapters – Early kings c84-1058; Canmore, 1058-1290; Bruce, 1290-1371; Stewart, 1371-1625; and three realm Stewarts 1625-1714. It is well indexed, referenced, and illustrated, including a central 16pp in colour. The four authors include Stirling's Michael Penman covering the 14th century period – and he has a book on David II in press.

# GLASGOW'S WATER SUPPLY

## Peter Joynson

Author's note: I have a copy in loose leaf form of the book presented on 15th February 1877 by the Lord Provost of Glasgow to Thomas Mason, Dean Convenor and Member of the Water Commission. My wife"s family is related to that Provost, Sir Robert Stewart. This large book gives a detailed illustrated account of the 1855 contract, and it seemed a useful idea to make available a readable precis of its most salient points.

*The book's story to 1877*

In 1842, the daughter of the Lord Provost of Glasgow died from typhoid from drinking the City's water. At that time Glasgow's water was pumped from the River Clyde, then little more than a stinking sewer. This tragedy spurred the Lord Provost to set up a Committee to investigate and put into place a pure water supply for the citizens of Glasgow.

In 1845, plans were put forward by the Glasgow Water Co. to use the Lochs of Lubnaig, Voil and Doune for this purpose and an Act of Parliament was obtained for the construction of the Works. On investigation, however, it was found that the Act did not provide sufficient storage in which to impound water to meet the great quantity required by Glasgow, together with the demands of the mill and fishing proprietors on the River Teith, and consequently the proposals fell to the ground.

Eight years later, in 1853. an Engineer named John Frederick Bateman was consulted by the Council. He saw at once the advantages of using Loch Katrine as the main source of water on account of its great storage capacity, amounting as it does to 9,000,000,000 gallons, which could be further increased by raising the Loch by 4 ft above its normal summer level. In addition to Loch Katrine, the Lochs of Vennacher and Drunkie could be included in the scheme, and their levels raised by 11 ft 9 inches and 25 ft respectively. These Lochs were never sought to supply Glasgow with any water, but rather, to supply the Compensation Water required by the Act of Parliament for the maintenance of the flow into the River Teith.

The watershed of Loch Katrine amounts to 23,000 acres or 36 square miles. The Loch is 367 ft above sea level with a maximum depth of 495 ft. The deepest loch in Scotland is Loch Morar being 1,009 ft maximum. Loch Ard is a mere 138 ft at its deepest.

The other great advantage of Loch Katrine is its proximity to the West Coast which intercepts the moist winds from the Atlantic. At the head of the Loch at Glengyle, the rainfall averages about 100 inches per year. Surrounded as it is, by the large peaks of Ben Venue and Ben Aan, the rain runs off the hard rocks with such rapidity and force that very little of it is lost by evaporation. There are only a few houses in the area and little or no cultivated land so that the water reaches the Loch in great purity. Any colouring of peat is quickly removed by oxidisation due to its long exposure in the Loch itself.

The source was thought to be right, but it took a huge amount of planning and preparation to work out the best way of getting the water out of Loch Katrine to the proposed Service Reservoir at Milngavie as the first stage, and as a second to convey it to Glasgow itself. The distance on stage one was 26 miles and stage two eight miles. Batemen surveyed the land and worked out the levels. A considerable task without the assistance of modern day equipment such as theodolites. He dug numerous investigation holes and found to his horror that much of the proposed route consisted of successive ridges containing the most difficult rocks separated by deep valleys. In addition there were no roads, tracks or building materials to hand, which would normally be considered as being essential in undertaking an engineering job of this magnitude.

Batemen came to the conclusion that ordinary surface construction was out of the question and tunnelling was the only possible solution for the aqueduct to be made to work. One of his major concerns was the water level in the ground, which, if arising from springs could in time do serious damage to the tunnelling and construction of shafts. Fortunately for him, no such problems were found as much of the under surface was slate into which no water penetrates. The problem of cost also concerned him. He had told the Council that the scheme would be cheap but he realised there could be considerable oncosts if due to the difficult conditions progress was slower than he had anticipated. In devising a route for the aqueduct he had to be sure that there was sufficient fall to convey the water through them. This he achieved with a drop of 10 inches to the mile.

Before the actual construction work could start on the 20th May 1856, a small village made of timber and turf had to be built complete with a church and a school near the head of Loch Chon to accommodate the workers. It became known as Sebastopol on account of the incessant noise from the blasting operations which continued day and night for three years. Almost everything had to be done by either horse or hand, and the bay near where the horses were kept was christened Midden Bay and is known as such to this day.

It was decided that water would be drawn from Loch Katrine almost three miles from its head at Glengyle. Sixty or more drills were constantly in use on the various faces of the route and where the rock was hardest a new drill or chisel had to be used for every inch of depth. Progress in some areas was very slow averaging not much more than eight yards a month.

About six miles from Loch Katrine the line of the aqueduct passed near the top of Loch Ard behind Couligarton. Here the ground was very broken requiring the building of a bridge 372 ft long and 47 ft 6 inches high. Further on a bridge over the Duchray Water was 462 ft long and 56 ft high and longest of all over the Kelty being 996 ft in length. The stretch of aqueduct near Couligarton was known as The Blairliullichan Contract. It cost £24,000 a mile, a sum which included the building of the Royal Cottage and other cottages.

The number of people working on the contract was about 3,000 men excluding inspectors and mechanics. Of the 26 miles between Loch Katrine and the Service Reservoir at Mugdock near Milngavie, 13 miles were tunnelling, three-and-a-half miles of iron piping and the remainder in arched aqueducts. The accuracy of this work was an amazing feat. The difference between the levels taken for Parliamentary purposes under the Act at the start and those subsequently taken at the end, was only about quarter of an inch in the 26 miles.

The Service Reservoir at Mugdock is about quarter of a mile from Milngavie and eight miles from Glasgow. It has a surface area of 62 acres with a mean depth of 50 ft, Capacity of 548,000,000 gallons or a supply to the City of 18 days in 1855. The water from the Reservoir was conveyed to Glasgow by four lines of 36 inch pipes.

On the 14th October 1859, Queen Victoria accompanied by Prince Albert and their two daughters Princess Alice and Princess Helena were present at the opening ceremony at the entrance to the aqueduct on Loch Katrine and opened the sluice which admitted the water. It poured with rain and the Royal party later had tea in the Royal Cottage. Later in the month, the Corporation gave John Bateman a banquet as a tribute to his genius and skill.

On 29th December 1859, the first water was introduced to a portion of the City and by March 1860 the whole City was included, and the pumping engines which for over 50 years had drawn water from the River Clyde were switched off. Thus Glasgow got its pure water supply at a cost of just under £2 million, the work was completed in less than half the time it took to build the Channel Tunnel in the present century.

*Developments in brief subsequent to the book and 1877*

Obviously after the plans laid down in 1855 for the supply of water to Glasgow, the population of the City increased each year. Measures had to be taken to account for this and in 1885, James Gale, the Chief Engineer and father of one of the late owners of Daldrishaig House, Aberfoyle, recommended that the level of Loch Katrine be raised by a further five feet. Consequently a second aqueduct was built which was two-and-a-half miles shorter than the first one and almost wholly underground. This work entailed raising the road on the North shore; building a new Stronachlacher Hotel; raising the 17th Century McGregor Burial Ground at Portnellan and building a wall around the small island near Stronachlachar Pier. This was the island where Rob Roy was said to have imprisoned the Duke of Montrose's Factor and relieved him of his collected rents.

In 1909, the level of Loch Arklet was raised by 22 ft increasing the size of the Loch from 207 acres to 551 acres. The waters of this Loch, less five million gallons of Compensation water into Loch Lomond, was channelled into Loch Katrine. This contract was completed just before the First World War in 1914. It entailed a lot of work as the public road had to be deviated and a large dam

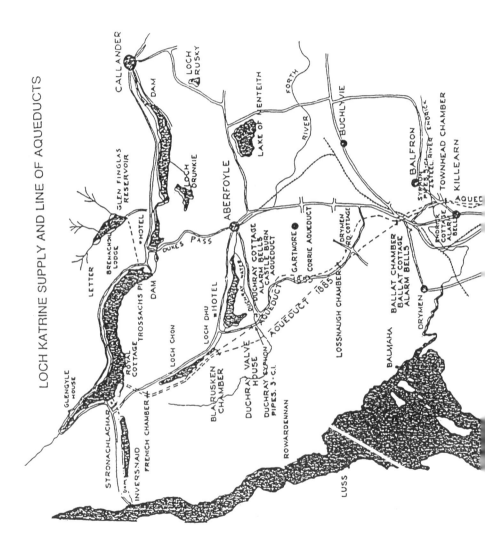

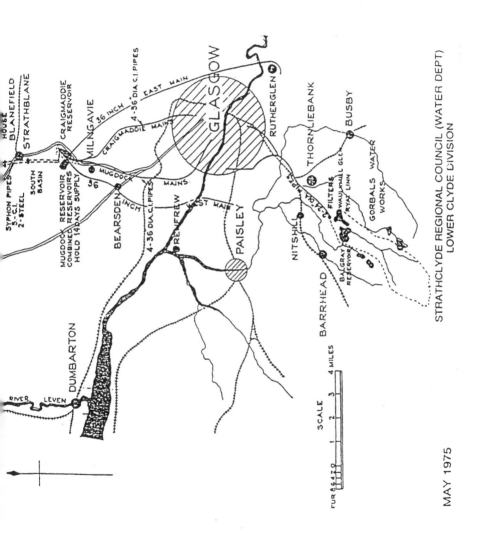

STRATHCLYDE REGIONAL COUNCIL (WATER DEPT)
LOWER CLYDE DIVISION

MAY 1975

had to be built at the outlet end of the Loch where it enters the Snaid Burn. The contractors experienced great problems in getting materials to the dam as they had to bring them by train to Balloch, by barge to Inversnaid and then over the hill by horse and makeshift electric aerial railway. After the war, in 1919, Loch Katrine was raised again by another 5 ft which required taking a new road and bridge between Stronachlacher and Glengyle House. The shepherds cottage at *Dubh of Glengyle* was demolished and a new one erected further up the hill. The McGregor Burial Ground had to be raised yet again and a completely new road on the North side of the Loch was built at a cost of £185,000.

In 1920, the Corporation bought the whole of the watersheds at Loch Katrine and Loch Arklet, extending to nearly 25,000 acres, from the Duke of Montrose at a cost of £77,000. In 1933, the water carrying capacity of two bridges on the second aqueduct was increased and in 1940, a subsidiary underwater sluice together with a salmon ladder was built at the sluices (near the Trossachs Pass) in case the original one was bombed in the Second World War. In 1960, the Loch at Glenfinlas was dammed and a two-and-a-half mile aqueduct built to feed the water into Loch Katrine.

Although the existing scheme has served the people of Glasgow well for over 140 years, and the quality of the water has been regarded as very good, it unfortunately does not fully meet the stringent requirements of water quality legislation introduced in 1990. A new treatment works is now planned for Milngavie. Construction may begin in 2002, to be completed in 2005, and cost £98 million. The plans may have aroused considerable environmental concerns.

*Selected sources*

1  Glasgow Water 1175 to the Present: an audio visual presentation by Paul Maxwell, West of Scotland Water, 2000.
2  BBC 2 programme of 26 June 2000 on 100 years of the Sir Walter Scott steamer and a brief history of Glasgow's water since 1860.
3  Water from the Tap: a video by Fasih Kahn et al, Strathclyde Water – presented to the 20th FNH 1994 – Man and the Landscape symposium 'Waters of central Scotland'.
4  J F Bateman in *Early Victorian Water Engineers* by J Binnie. 1981.
5  J F Bateman (1810-89) Water Engineer. P Russell. *Transactions of the Newcomen Society* 52, 1981.
6  On Loch Katrine water purity … lead pipes, discontinued since 1968 … Richards et al. *Journal of the Institution of Water Engineers and Scientists* 34, July 1980, 315-33.
7  Glasgow Corporation Waterworks. J R Sutherland. *Transactions of the Institute of Water Engineers* 29, 1924, 53-6.
8  On the Glasgow Waterworks. J M Gale. *Institution of Engineers in Scotland* 11, 1863-4, p45.

# THE TROSSACHS IN ART

## Louis Stott

There is no doubt that the Trossachs have appeared too often on chocolate boxes, or they seem as if they have. Hugh Quigley, who was born in Stirling, describes the Trossachs as follows:

"... their beauty has become conventional and perhaps rather wearisome. They provide models for regular 'beauty' pictures of the type which used to fill postcard albums, and they are still too reminiscent of the golden harmonies of the early English schools of painting. "

*The Highlands of Scotland* 1936

However, although many conventional and, on that account, uninspiring landscapes may have been drawn, and painted in the Trossachs, it is also a district which great artists have visited, and there executed important works. It was because a notable artist was visiting the district that Patrick Graham, Minister of the Parish and the friend of Scott, compiled what was one of the first guides to Aberfoyle and Strathard. In a preface Graham relates how he first put the description together in 1792 for a visit by **Joseph Farington** (1747-1821), one of the most influential British artists of the late eighteenth and early nineteenth centuries, who was engaged in making some sketches of the Forth for what proved to be an abortive publication. Farington commented:

A stranger must feel himself uncommonly struck on meeting, at the very back of Ben Lomond, in a spot so sequestered as to be almost unknown to the world, a scene like the present; an extensive sheet of water, skirted with woods and cultivated fields, and accompanied with every object essential to picturesque beauty; the whole grouped and diversified in a style of harmony which may be thought by some to rival the scenes presented by the Cumberland lakes.

Farington's comparison with the English Lake District is frequently echoed by later writers. Such parallels owe their origin to Thomas Gray and William Gilpin who, along with Boswell and Johnson, were amongst the first travellers to visit Scotland in the eighteenth century which, at the time, was far less well known than places on the continent visited during the course of the 'Grand Tour'. The Lake District had already been 'discovered', and the comparison was natural enough, although it tends to aggravate most Scots. The Wordsworths were by far the most prone to draw these parallels, and they were almost always, quite unfairly, to the disadvantage of the Scottish countryside.

## Turner

It was Farington who advised Turner about his early visits to Scotland in 1797 and 1801 which produced some of his greatest British works, but the great man did not visit Loch Ard until 1831. **Joseph Mallord William Turner** (1775-1857) is generally regarded as Britain's greatest landscape artist. Unlike Loch Katrine, Loch Ard did not produce any famous finished works, but his *Loch Ard*

*Sketch Book* contains notable drawings of Aberfoyle, Craigmore, the Queen's View and Loch Ard. In their way they are quite as impressive as his better-known drawings of other parts of the Trossachs. Robert Cadell (1788-1849), Scott's publisher friend, had arranged that Turner should illustrate Lockhart's edition of Scott's *Poetical Works* (1834), and Turner outlined his plans to Scott, who offered him a pony for the duration of his visit. In fact, Scott found Turner a pain in the neck. He was, by 1831 highly regarded, and demanding of his host, as here:

> Therefore, do pray say how long do you think it will take me to collect the materials in your neighbourhood. Many are near but my bad horsemanship puts your kind offer of a pony, I fear, out of the account in shortening the time, and when I get as far as Loch Katrine I shall not like to turn back without Staffa, Mull and all. A steamboat is now established to the Western Isles, so I have heard lately, and therefore much of the difficulty becomes removed, but being wholly unacquainted with the distance I will thank you to say what time will be absolutely wanting.

Turner, not wishing to opt for pony trekking, opted for public transport and almost certainly followed one of the formal Trossachs Tours. It was **William Miller** (1796-1882) of Edinburgh, who produced a number of Turneresque watercolours on his own account, who engraved Turner's illustrations of Loch Katrine and Loch Achray (Figure 1). The selection of suitable subjects proved problematical with Turner's sketches – *Inchcailleach, Bealach nam Bo,* and *Coir nan Uruiskin* all being considered as possibilities. In the end *Loch Katrine* constituted the frontispiece, and *Loch Achray,* the vignette.

Turner's *Loch Ard Sketch Book* contains numerous drawings of Loch Vennacher, Ben Venue, Aberfoyle and Loch Ard. There can be no criticism of Turner's exquisite drawings, but his only oil connected with the district signally failed to attract the approbation of the sternest critic of the period, John Ruskin. The painting entitled *The Trossachs* is sometimes dated 1799-1800, although Turner's first substantive visit to Scotland was not until 1801. The picture was first called *Mountain Landscape with a Lake* and it is now in the Fitzwilliam Museum, Cambridge. It is a striking picture, but Ruskin lambasted it:

> The worst picture I ever saw of this period, the Trossachs, has been for some time exhibited at Mr Grundy's in Regent Street; and it has been much praised in the public press on the ground, I suppose, that it exhibits so little of Turner's power or manner as to be hardly recognisable as one of his works.

Turner is probably the most important artist to be associated with the district, but he was not, of course, the first. Artists anxious to illustrate the scenery they described, one of the first of whom was Farington, soon followed the earliest literary visitors to Loch Lomond, like William Gilpin, an illustrator himself. Indeed, eighteenth century literary visitors identified 'stations' from which the best views might be obtained which became the viewpoints from which people came to expect painters and engravers to depict the scenery. There can be no doubt that such outstanding points of view exist, but this practice has led to an element of repetitiveness, and perhaps to an attendant lack of imagination in landscape painting in the Trossachs. However, it has also meant that individual artists have striven to achieve different effects in the same place, and have been able to assume that the public were familiar with their subject.

## Early Artists

The most interesting of the early illustrators to depict the Trossachs were probably **Alexander Campbell** (1764-1824) and **George Fennel Robson** (1788-1833). Campbell, from the foot of Loch Lubnaig, was a local man, and he put several Trossachs scenes which later became standard views in his *Journey Through Parts of North Britain*. It was published in 1802, before the Wordsworths visited the Trossachs, and before Scott had made them famous. These views included drawings – *Ben Ledi, Loch-vana-choir, Loch Achray, Cori-nan-Urishin, Loch Kaitrin, East-end, Loch Kaitrin, West-end,* and *Hill of Binion from the Lake*. Campbell is an important figure, a songwriter of distinction, highly esteemed by Scott, who is rather neglected. Robson's *The Scenery of the Grampian Mountains* of 1814 included views of Ben Lomond both from Loch Ard (Figure 2), and, much less usual, from above Loch Katrine and several other Trossachs scenes. **James Skene** (1775-1864) illustrated scenes from the Waverley Novels including the *Fort of Inversnaid, Ledard,* the *Ford of Alianan, Lochard* and the *Clachan of Aberfoil.* Episodes from the novels attracted famous illustrators such as **George Cruikshank** (1792-1878) who depicted *The Fray at Jean MacAlpine's Inn* and **Sam Bough** (1822-78) who showed *The Escape of Rob Roy at the Ford.* Bough was a pupil for a short time of perhaps the most prolific of nineteenth century illustrators of mountain scenery **Thomas Allom** (1804-72) who drew several local scenes which appeared in *Scotland Illustrated* [1835]. Joseph Swan's *Scottish Lakes* [1834.] included drawings of Loch Ard, Loch Katrine and the Loch of Monteith drawn by **J. Fleming** (1792-1845).

Landscape painters were not much in evidence in the Trossachs in the eighteenth century, but by the early nineteenth century they were. **Alexander Nasmyth** (1758-1840), one of the most famous of Scotland's eighteenth century landscape artists, executed a number of essentially Scottish paintings late in life (Figure 3). His earlier work is Italian in its inspiration. **John Knox** (1778-1845), his pupil and the artist who painted the sensational views from the summit of Ben Lomond which can be seen in the Kelvingrove Art Gallery, Glasgow, painted a picture called *Highland Loch Scene* (Figure 4) held at Pollock House, Glasgow that is generally considered to be of Loch Katrine and was, perhaps, an imitation of Nasmyth's work. A lesser master, much associated with Highland landscapes, was **James Stevenson** (d. 1844) who exhibited several works showing less usual scenes at the Royal Scottish Academy.

**John Thomson of Duddingston** (1778-1840) followed his friend Sir Walter Scott into the Trossachs, and exhibited *Loch Katrine from Coir-nan-Uriskin* in 1823. William Baird, who recorded Thomson's work, stated:

"If one would realise the aspect of the Trossachs presented to Sir Walter Scott when he wrote his Lady of the Lake, before it had been invaded by the modern tourist, with roadways, hotels and piers for their convenience, he must see this picture."

Another famous painter who touched on the Trossachs was **Edwin Landseer** (1802-73), who exhibited *The River Teith, Perthshire* at the Royal

Institution in 1826. His 1824 portrait of Sir Walter Scott, painted at Abbotsford, is one of the best liked.

## Ruskin and Millais

In 1853 **John Ruskin** (1819-1900), his wife Effie, and **John Everett Millais** (1829-96), stayed in the village of Brig o' Turk, which gets its name from an eighteenth century bridge, carefully widened and restored in the 1930s, over the burn which flows through Glenfinglas. It was here that Millais fell in love with Effie whose marriage with Ruskin had not been consummated. When Effie later left Ruskin and married Millais, the biggest scandal since Byron's day broke.

The little river Turk still rushes down a fine gorge where there are four waterfalls. In spate the nineteenth century atmosphere of the clachan can still be recaptured, but the gorge is dominated nowadays by a spectacular dam. Although he had been to the Trossachs in 1838 with his parents, it was probably the associations of the place with Scott that drew Ruskin to Brig o' Turk in 1853 with his wife, whom he had married five years previously, and his protégé, Millais. In 1879 Ruskin exhibited a picture of the view from the Silver Strand entitled *Loch Katrine, looking to Coir nan Uriskin, July 23 1838*. In 1853 Ruskin made some famous drawings of the rocks he found in the bed of the Turk:

> Yesterday drawing on the rocks by the stream. Everett still ill with headache. The skies all turquoise and violet, melted in dew; and heavenly bars of delicate cloud behind Ben Venue in the evening.
> This morning grey with heavy clouds low on the hills......
> John Ruskin *Letters* 20th July, 1853

Millais also began one of his most famous pictures (Figure 5), in which one of the waterfalls on the Turk was to form the background to a portrait of Ruskin, but he did not complete it until the following year. He also painted a picture of Effie beside a waterfall in the glen, and his sketch book is a delightful record of what was, in spite of wet weather, a varied holiday. The portrait of Ruskin, the difficulty of its execution and, above all, the blossoming romance between Effie and Millais dominate the letters which the three wrote to their family and friends. Mary Lutyens used them as the basis for her delightful biography *Millais and the Ruskins* (1967). At the beginning of the holiday Millais was an admirer of Effie, and worshipped Ruskin; by the end of it he was complaining about Ruskin and hopelessly in love with Effie. The following letter from Millais to Holman Hunt, which refers to Millais' brother, William, captures the atmosphere:

> The last four days we have had incessant rain, swelling the streams to torrents, This afternoon we all walked to see some of the principal waterfalls which in colour resemble XXX stout. The roads are deeper in water than the Wandle so we were walking ankle deep. The dreariness of mountainous country in wet weather is beyond everything. I have employed myself making little studies of Mrs Ruskin whilst William has given way to whisky and execration. Having the acquaintance of Mrs Ruskin is a blessing, Her husband is a good fellow but not of our kind, his soul is always with the clouds and out of reach of ordinary Mortals – I mean that he theorises about the vastness of space and

looks at a lovely little stream in practical contempt, I have had a canvas and box made in Edinburgh to paint his portrait overlooking a waterfall. I think it will be fine as it quite suits his character and the background of the foaming water, rocks and clasping roots look splendid behind his placid figure.

In another letter Millais refers to midges, a considerable hazard to plein air painters in the Trossachs:

When the weather permits, we all dine out upon the rocks, Mrs Ruskin working, her husband drawing, and myself painting, there is only one drawback to this almost perfect happiness - the midges, They bite so dreadfully that it is beyond human endurance to sit quiet, therefore many a splendid day passes without being able to work.

William Millais, who was also an artist, gives a vivid description of a Glenfinglas Sabbath:

How well I remember our going to the little free kirk, arrayed as well-turned out Highland men. The service was to us somewhat comical and we could hardly stay it out. The precentor was a little very bow-legged old man, with the wheeziest of voices, and sang the first line of the paraphrase alone, whilst his little shaggy terrier, the image of his master, joined in in a piteous howl, The other lines were sung by the congregation, assisted by a few collies. I afterwards tackled the little precentor, and asked him why he didn't have an organ, 'Ah man, would you have us take to the devil's band?' was his answer.

When the sermon came, it was most amusing to us to watch the old men passing their ram's horn snuff-mills to one another, and putting little bone spades full of the pungent material up their noses to keep them awake.

In front of us were two well-dressed young girls) in all the newest fashion, and when the offertory-box was poked towards them, they put in a farthing. We afterwards saw them take off their shoes and stockings and walk home barefooted.

J.S. Millais *Life and Letters of Millais* 1899

Everett Millais and his brother William often wore the kilt, to the amusement of the local inhabitants. This had a highly amusing artistic consequence. The famous French animal painter **Rosa Bonheur** (1822-1899) came to the Highlands, inspired by Landseer's Highland stags. After visiting the cattle fair at Stenhousemuir, where she obtained much subject matter, she came to the Trossachs anxious to espy a native in a kilt. The first such person she saw was Millais. Rosa Bonheur and her companion were accompanied by the picture dealer and publisher Gambart who introduced them:

"Ah, my dear Millais, Mademoiselle Rosa Bonheur has been eagerly on the look-out for the Highland garb ever since we left Edinburgh, and yours is the first kilt she has seen. You are immortalised."

Millais filled two sketch books containing highly finished drawings and sketches when he was in Glenfinglas with Ruskin including *A Fishing Party on Loch Achray* and *The Kirk in Glenfinlas* (Figure 6). After his marriage to Effie Gray in June 1855, Millais took the manse of Brig o' Turk in Glenfinglas in August, 1856. Here, after an interval of shooting and fishing, "… he painted a small portrait of the minister – a hard-featured and by no means prepossessing Celt." (J.G. Millais)

**McCulloch and others**

Knox's most famous pupil was **Horatio McCulloch** (1805-1867) who is the most evocative of Scottish mountain landscape painters. His masterpiece, so far as this district is concerned, is *Loch Katrine* [1866] (Figure 7), a stunning picture of Ellen's Isle and Ben Venue from the same point of view as Turner chose. Alexander Fraser, McCulloch's pupil, biographer and friend, records that he was in the Trossachs in the Autumn of 1861 when he probably executed studies for this picture. Alexander Smith, the poet and author of *A Summer in Skye*, commented "As a view of Highland scenery we have never seen its equal, and no man but McCulloch could have produced it." McCulloch executed two other major works showing Ben Venue, this time from Loch Achray, when he stayed at the Manse in 1863. The Minister, William Wilson, clearly impressed with his piety, reported that when he had finished one of his major oils, McCulloch said, "I have just finished my picture. Leave me alone for a few minutes. Whenever I finish a big picture, I offer a word of thanks to the Most High."

McCulloch's rivals at this time included the prolific **Sam Bough** (1822-78), **Edmund Crawford** (1806-1885), **Arthur Perigal** (1816-1884), and **John Adam Houston** (1812-1864) all of whom worked in the Trossachs at one time and another. Bough's real forte was watercolour, but he also painted oils. He seems to have been in Strathgartney on several occasions in the late 1860s at the same time as McCulloch. The Hunterian Museum, Glasgow acquired his watercolour *River Teith at Callander with Ben Ledi in the Distance* dated 1879. Perigal's work *In the Trossachs* derives from an earlier period between 1837 and 1844. Another mid century landscape painter who was very fond of Loch Achray was **Waller Hugh Paton** (1828-1895), a pupil of Houston associated with the Pre-Raphaelites, who often achieved his effects by a more intimate approach. **James Hall Cranstoun** (1821-1907) was a Perthshire artist whose subjects included the favourite *Ben Ledi from Callander*. **Thomas Stuart Smith** (1815-69), whose bequest led to the establishment of an art gallery, the Smith Institute in Stirling, painted *Ben Ledi in Winter* (Figure 8).

In *The Trossachs in Literature and Tradition* Wilson also mentions *Loch Katrine* by James Docharty (1829-1878) of Bonhill, the painter of realistic, true to life pictures of the Highlands. Docharty was influenced by McCulloch and Milne Donald, and frequently came to the Trossachs. Other works of Docharty's include *Loch Vennachar looking towards Callander* [1868], and *Heart of the Trossachs* [1868]. Wilson also records pictures by **John MacWhirter** (1839-1911), the Academician much praised by Ruskin, and **Colin Hunter** (1841-1904), the pupil of James Milne Donald noted for his watercolours. However, the painter who seems to have impressed him most was **John Smart** RSA (1838-1899) whose pictures demonstrated his ardent passion for his native land (David and Francina Irwin). His *A Perthshire River* [1894], of the Teith with Doune Castle in the distance, is in the Smith Art Gallery. Wilson said his best picture was *The Heat of the Day*, of Loch Achray. In 1877/8 he was at Aberfoyle painting *View near Kinlochard, Moor near Port of Menteith: Rain Coming On*, and *Rain Clouds crossing* *the Valley near Aberfoyle.* The Dundee Art Gallery has Smart's 1886 picture *The Pass of Leny, Perthshire.* This is inscribed on the back as follows:

> When the hilltops are whitened wi' winter's first sna',
> And the leaves o' the summer are fading awa'

The plein air painter **Alexander Fraser** (1827-1899), who achieved similar effects to those of McCulloch and Bough rather later, was also in the Trossachs at this point. His contemporary, the Stirling-born artist **Thomas Clark** (1820-76), lived at Dundarroch, the beautiful house on a promontory at the foot of Loch Ard. He painted mainly Scottish scenes, though not many of his subjects were local.

## The Glasgow Boys

Perhaps it was the connection with Ruskin that led the Glasgow Boys to Brig o' Turk in 1879-81, but it was probably its character as the nearest 'Highland clachan' (in contrast to the estate villages of Luss and Gartmore) to Glasgow that attracted them. They were not, however, interested in painting 'scenery', but interested in painting rural life truthfully. In any case it is agreed that the summers they spent together in the Trossachs (and at Rosneath and Cockburnspath) were critical to their development as artists, not so much for what they produced as for the conversations about painting which they had. Guthrie drew Joseph Crawhall, himself and Walton sharing a bottle of wine which captured their spirit of fellowship which they enjoyed at Brig o' Turk.

**James Guthrie** (1859-1930) was a central figure, and is one of the best known of the Glasgow Boys. He went with Walton to Brig o' Turk in 1879 where Crawhall joined them. He produced a sketch called *A Highland Shepherd* and an oil *The Camp in the Wood* in 1879. In 1881 he executed a darkly lit oil painting *Gypsy Fires are Burning for Daylight's Past and Gone,* and made drawings for his most famous picture *A Funeral Service in the Highlands,* a notable painting of a grim scene which he witnessed at Brig o' Turk, and which he finished using models in a studio in Helensburgh. **Joseph Crawhall** (1861-1913) was a brilliant animal painter with a great love of horses. This gave him a common interest with Robert Bontine Cunninghame Graham in nearby Gartmore, and Graham wrote an affectionate sketch of him, but none of his work has been particularly attributed to the Trossachs. **George Henry** (1858-1943), was a young pupil of W.Y. MacGregor, who joined Guthrie and Crawhall at Brig o' Turk in 1881, and painted *The Cottage on the Hill* and a charming picture called *Brig o' Turk* – to be seen in Glasgow – which he finished in 1882. **Edward Arthur Walton** (1860-1922) painted 'rural' subjects. His fine 1879 picture *The Brig o' Turk* is in Dundee Art Gallery. In 1881 he executed *The Wayfarer* at Glenfinglas. **William York Macgregor** (1855-1923), a pupil of James Docharty, had a life studio in Bath Street where the Glasgow Boys met regularly. He was thus regarded as a senior member of the group. When his health deteriorated in 1886, he moved to Albyn Lodge in the little spa town of Bridge of Allan on the fringes of the Trossachs. Indeed Stirling, from which the Trossachs were easily accessible, became another focal point for the Glasgow Boys.

The Scottish Academician **Joseph Denovan Adam** (1842-1896) was a Glasgow landscape painter who later moved to Crieff, who, in 1887, established a studio on a small farm at Craigmill, Stirling, and who finally settled at Balkerach, Callander. Adam was famous for painting Highland Cattle, and taught other artists to paint these beasts at Craigmill, which became a focal point for artistic activity. As a landscape painter, Adam exhibited a number of Trossachs subjects at the Royal Scottish Academy late in life. It is a curiosity that one of Adam's pupils at Craigmill was Edith Holden, whose book *Diary of An Edwardian Lady* enjoyed a run of success in the 1980s. Visitors to Craigmill included **William Kennedy** (1859-1918), another of the Glasgow Boys, who met his wife there, and it is considered probable that he brought Joseph Crawhall and John Lavery to Craigmill. Kennedy stayed in Abbey Road, Stirling and it was probably he who suggested Cambuskenneth to the others. Walton had a studio in the village after 1888, Guthrie lodged there, and Henry visited the district, to stay with Kennedy, as did other members of this network of painters. In the summer of 1887 Arthur Melville, Crawhall and Walton went to Stirling. **Arthur Melville** (1855-1904) the leading Scottish Impressionist took a studio at the back of a grocery shop in Cambuskenneth. He had followed Guthrie, Henry and Walton in going to Brig o' Turk, and he exhibited pictures entitled *Loch Vennacher* and *The Shieling, Brig o' Turk* in 1884. Other artists who were contemporaries of the Glasgow Boys who were working in the Trossachs at the same time in what was, perhaps, a more old-fashioned way included **George Aikman** (1830-1905), **George Whitton Johnstone** (1849-1901), and the Perthshire artist **Duncan Cameron** (1837-1916), whose picture *Loch Achray and Ben Venue* [1880] is in Dundee Art Gallery. The popular **Charles Martin Hardie** (1858-1916) made Menteith the setting for a number of genre paintings including *An Unrecorded Coronation, Inchmahome, Isle of Rest, AD 1548.*

(Sir) **John Lavery** (1856-1941), another leading figure among the Glasgow Boys, was a famous portrait painter, although also skilled in other branches of his art. He could and did paint landscapes, but he was not at Glenfinglas with the other Glasgow Boys in 1879/81. However, both he and Crawhall were friendly with Cunninghame Graham and, in 1895, he went to Gartmore to paint two portraits of him. Lavery was a man of elegance and wit, and a very distinguished painter who has left a delightful account of his experiences there:

John Burns had joined us on this occasion at Gartmore, for it was just at this time that they had both come out of Pentonville, where they had served six weeks' hard labour for their share in the Trafalgar Square riots over the question of free speech – the two of then taking on, so they claimed, single-handed, the constabulary numbering five thousand, I asked them about their experiences in prison, hard labour they considered less irksome than ordinary imprisonment, for with the former you were given plenty of coarse food, and time passed; while with the latter you were starved and left to pass the time in contemplation, There was a parson in the next cell to him, said Graham, who was in for 'an old ecclesiastical failing'. Burns was very proud of his biceps which he exposed, and Graham equally so of his agility with the foils, which he demonstrated from time to time with the aid of his walking-stick as we strolled in the cool of the evening,

Graham purchased from the tramway company a wild Argentine pony that refused to go into harness. He named him Pampa, and insisted on my painting a picture of himself in complete cowboy outfit on the pacing steed. Then I painted him frankly in the manner full-length and life-size, a harmony in brown, which he christened *Don Roberto, Commander for the King of Aragon in the Two Sicilies.* The equestrian group he presented to Buenos Ayres, and the Commander was purchased by the Corporation of Glasgow. It was concerning the latter that Bernard Shaw said, "He is, I understand, a Spanish hildago, hence the superbity of his portrait by Lavery (Velasquez being no longer available). He is, I know, a Scottish laird. How he continues to be authentically the two things at the same time is no more intelligible to me than the fact that everything that has ever happened to him seemed to have happened in Paraguay or Texas instead of Spain or Scotland."

When I knew him at this time his finances were in a shocking state, and things were getting unbearable down at Gartmore. Suddenly he wrote to say that he could stand it no longer, Would I come down at once and see him end it all with Pampa, in a spot where I had painted a view of the Rob Roy Country that he loved? I wired back, "Ill in bed, wait till next week," Thus I postponed his death for forty years.

Sir John Lavery A Painter's Life 1940

The portrait referred to by Shaw, who used Cunninghame Graham as a prototype for Bluntschli in *Arms and the Man,* is in the Kelvingrove Art Gallery, Glasgow. They also have a small bronze head of Cunninghame Graham by **Jacob Epstein**. Lavery's *Loch Katrine* (Figure 9) was his only full-blown Scottish landscape, and dates from 1913. It was presented to the National Gallery of Scotland. This painting, of the Silver Strand and Ben Venue, unlike so many others of the same subject, is a fresh statement of the familiar.

By far the most distinguished twentieth century painter and illustrator associated with the Trossachs is sometimes considered to be one of the Glasgow Boys too. He was **David Young Cameron** (1865-1945) who lived at one time at Kirkhill, and then at Dun Eaglais, Kippen. His house commands what is undoubtedly the finest distant prospect of the Southern Highlands; the horned peak of Ben Lomond, Ben Venue, the pyramidal Ben Ledi, and the striking pair Stuc a Chroin and Ben Vorlich rise impressively across the Vale of Mentieth. Cameron was a fine oil painter whose dramatic painting *Ben Ledi, Spring* is in the Tate Gallery. The Smith Art Gallery has a small oil, *Ben Venue* by Cameron. He was, however, perhaps best known for his exquisite etchings which include a very fine series of Ben Lomond from Loch Ard (Figure 10) and other Trossachs subjects. As an illustrator he collaborated most effectively with Seton Gordon providing dozens of blocks for *Highways and Byways in the Central Highlands*. His etching *Doon Hill* was used as the frontispiece for Cunninghame Graham's edition of *The Secret Commonwealth*.

Cameron's contemporary, the Scottish Academician **Archibald Kay** (1860-1935) lived at Woodend, Kilmahog near Callander, as well as having a studio in Glasgow. He was President of the Glasgow Art Club, and, like a number of the Glasgow Boys, he had attended the Academy Julian in Paris, but he was always a more old-fashioned artist than they were. Kay was a vigorous and very productive landscape painter, with a particular flair for river scenes (Figure 11). The river Leny was a favourite subject of his. Of his numerous other works it can be noted that he exhibited in 1932 a painting of *The New Road to the Trossachs* depicting a dramatic change in his native place. Two other important twentieth century painters, **Thomas Campbell Mackie** (1887-1952) and **Mary Armour** [Steel] (b. 1902), both of whom lived in Milngavie, have works derived from the Trossachs represented in the Kelvingrove Gallery. Other lesser artists at work during the twentieth century, have included **William Douglas MacLeod** (1892-1963) and **Alfred de Breanski** (1852-1928).

## Sculpture

Just outside Callander, superbly situated on a little hill, is the graveyard of the clan most associated with the district, the Buchanans, and there is a monument to a poet who was a native of Ardoch, Strathyre, **Dugald Buchanan** (1716-1768). His memorial plaque reads as follows:

> *Dugald Buchanan*
> *Gaelic Poet Teacher Evangelist*
> 1716-1768
> This monument marks his resting place,
> and commemorates his gifts of inspired
> language and sacred song by which
> the literature of his native Highlands has
> been enriched.
>
> An Fhuil a dhiol do cheartas teann
> S'a dhoirteadh air a chrann gu lar
> S'ann aisd tha mearbsa O m Righ
> Nach dit thum anam air sgath.
>
> Pittendrigh Macgillivray Erected 1925

A version of the Gaelic is as follows: "The blood that repayed Your firm justice was shed on the ground from the Cross. It is from it, O King, that I trust that you will not condemn my soul."

**James Pittendrigh Macgillivray** (1856-1938), another of the Glasgow Boys, was a Poet, King's Sculptor in Ordinary for Scotland, and Principal of the Edinburgh School of Art. He almost certainly both wrote the inscription and carved the plaque.

Earlier a statue of *Rob Roy* [1883], now in the grounds of a private house, commissioned by John Aird, was sculpted by **Thomas Stuart Burnet** (1853-1888) for which George Whitton Johnstone, the landscape painter, was the model. More recently **Benno Schotz** (1891-1984), also Royal Sculptor-in-Ordinary, executed what is probably the liveliest statue of Rob Roy, erected in Stirling in 1975 (Figure 12). As the sculptor relates it was the subject of some controversy:

> Early in May, 1972 I received a visit from a Mr Adam MacGregor Dick of Kilmarnock, He was a distant descendant of Rob Roy, albeit on the wrong side of the blanket, at least this is how he put it, he wanted to commission a statue of his famous antecedent..... He brought me what was purported to be a contemporary portrait, which he wished me to copy. It represented Rob Roy as a dandy, in a dancing rather than a fighting pose. I told Mr Dick that if he wanted me to carry out the commission, I would make Rob Roy a man of action, the man he was, though not as one ready for attack, I would represent him with

his sword at the ready, in defence of his right, full of confidence in his power and proud in his stance.

At that time he intended the statue for Kilmarnock, but friends suggested Edinburgh. As a site there did not materialise, he approached Stirling, who provided a fine site in their town centre. However, I was happy to continue in the meantime with my maquettes and full scale figure, in spite of much friction between Mr Dick and myself.......as has often been the case, I underestimated my costs.....

My design for the plinth was rejected in favour of one by the Stirling town architect; I was not even invited to see that the statue was properly erected, by which time Mr Dick had died. To add insult to injury, his widow would not allow Stirling District Council to invite me to the unveiling.

## Early Photographers In The Trossachs

While steel engravings were a very important method of book illustration, it was the advent of such processes as chromolithography which meant that by the end of the nineteenth century coloured reproductions of scenes from the Trossachs, not always by the most competent artists, became common-place, and photography came to replace landscape painting of a certain kind. Appropriately enough the Trossachs played a small part in the history of photography.

**Willliam Henry Fox Talbot** (1800-1877), the British 'inventor of photography' visited Loch Katrine in October 1844 to make Calotypes of scenery associated with Sir Walter Scott, and, in 1845, published *Sun Pictures in Scotland* which included views of, for example, Abbotsford, and the first photograph of the Scott Monument, then under construction in Edinburgh. There were six views of Loch Katrine, generally considered to be amongst his most interesting photographs.

**George Washington Wilson** (1823-93) of Aberdeen became Photographer Royal to Queen Victoria, and is generally considered to be the first landscape photographer. He exercised an influence comparable with that of Scott on the development of tourism in Scotland in the second half of the nineteenth century. His earliest photographs were of his native Deeside, but he rapidly extended his range and views in the Trossachs are amongst his earliest subjects. It was Wilson who established many very well known photographic points of view, but, equally, he frequently adopts interesting and original standpoints which have not been used by others. His views of the Pass of Bealach nam Bo and the Goblin's Cave are notable in this respect. He is known to have visited the Trossachs in 1859, and in 1861-63. An edition of *The Lady of the Lake* published by A&C Black in 1863 had photographic illustrations by Wilson. Dating his photographs is problematical, and is dealt with by Roger Taylor in his authoritative book *George Washington Wilson – Artist and Photographer* 1981.

## Selected Bibliography

| | | |
|---|---|---|
| Baird, William | *John Thomson of Duddingston pastor and painter* | (1895-1920) |
| Billcliffe, Roger | *The Glasgow Boys* | (1985) |
| Caw, Sir James | *Scottish Painting Past and Present* | (1908) |
| Devany, Maria | *Joseph Denovan Adam (1842-96), Animal Painter* | (1995) |
| Graham, Rev Patrick | *Sketches of Perthshire* | (1806) |
| Graham, R.B.C. (ed) | *The Secret Commonwealth* | (1933) |
| Hardie, William R. | *Scottish Painting 1837-1939* | (1976) |
| Irwin, David and Francina | *Scottish Painters at Home and Abroad* | (1974) |
| Lavery, Sir John | *A Painter's Life* | (1940) |
| Millais, J.S. | *Life and Letters of Millais* | (1899) |
| Quigley, Hugh | *Highlands of Scotland* | (1936) |
| Rinder, Frank | *Royal Scottish Academy 1826-1916* | (1975) |
| Salaman, M.C. | *Sir D.Y. Cameron* | (1925) |
| Wilson, William | *Trossachs in Literature and Tradition* | (1908) |

### Editor/Author Note

For illustrative figures we are as a small charity grateful for permissions given by some of the galleries in Appendix A.

Of added interest are Appendices B and C – Some prints and illustrations of the Trossachs – a check list (B). Some artists associated with the Trossachs (C) with their works.

Figure 1

Turner/Miller                                                                    Loch Katrine

So wondrous wild the whole might seem
The scenery of a fairy dream

Figure 2

Robson/Finders                                          Loch Ard and Ben Lomond

Figure 3

Nasmyth                                                    Highland Landscape

Figure 4

Knox                                                      Highland Loch Scene

Figure 5

Millais  John Ruskin

Figure 6

Millais  The Kirk, Glenfinlass

Figure 7

McCulloch                                                    Loch Katrine

Figure 8

Smith                                                        Ben Ledi in winter

Figure 9

Lavery                                    Loch Katrine

Figure 10

Cameron                                    Loch Ard

Figure 11

Kay                                                    O' river of winter sunshine

Figure 12

Schotz              Rob Roy

L. Corbett

## Appendix A

### Art Galleries Holdings

The works of some of the artists referred to can be seen in the following public collections, although they may not always be on show:

National Gallery of Scotland, Edinburgh
John Lavery                     *Loch Katrine*

Kelvingrove Gallery, Glasgow

| | |
|---|---|
| Joseph Denovan Adam | *December near Callander* |
| Mary Armour | *Ben Ledi* |
| Sam Bough | *Loch Achray* |
| James Docharty | *Heart of the Trossachs* |
| | *In The Trossachs* |
| Alexander Fraser | *Springtime, Dundarroch* |
| | *Brig o' Turk* |
| David Farquharson | *On the Achray* |
| Sir James Guthrie | *A Highland Funeral* |
| George Henry | *Brig o' Turk* |
| Sir John Lavery | *R. B. Cunninghame Graham* |
| Horatio McCulloch | *Loch Achray: Evening* |
| | *Loch Achray: Morning* |
| Thomas Campbell Mackie | *Ben Ledi* |
| Alexander Nasmyth | *Highland Landscape with Temple* |

Stirling Maxwell Collection, Pollock House, Glasgow

| | |
|---|---|
| John Knox | *Highland Loch Scene* |
| Alexander Nasmyth | *Highland Landscape* |

Hunterian Art Gallery, Hillhead, Glasgow University

| | |
|---|---|
| Sam Bough | *The River Teith at Callander(w)* |
| D.Y. Cameron | *Loch Achray* |

Perth Art Gallery

| | |
|---|---|
| James Cranstoun | *Ben Ledi from Callander* |
| Everett Galloway | *Loch Vennacher and Ben Venue from Invertrossachs(w)* |
| Horatio McCulloch | *Loch Katrine* |
| Jack Merriot | *Ben Venue(w)* |

Smith Art Gallery, Stirling

| | |
|---|---|
| D.Y. Cameron | *Ben Venue* |
| George Whitton Johnstone | *Lake of Menteith* |
| Archibald Kay | *O' river of winter sunshine* |
| John Smart | *A Perthshire River* |
| Thomas Stuart Smith | *Ben Ledi in Winter* |

Dundee Art Galleries

| | |
|---|---|
| Duncan Cameron | *Loch Achray and Ben Venue* |
| James Docharty | *The River Achray* |
| Sir Wm. Douglas | *On the Shores of the Lake of Menteith* |
| David Farquharson | *Loch Achray* |
| John Smart | *The Pass of Leny, Perthshire* |
| Edward Arthur Walton | *The Brig o' Turk* |

## Appendix B
### Prints and Illustrations of the Trossachs: A Checklist

**1. Illustrations of Scott's Novels**
Four in ROB ROY  ND (=not dated)
*The Pass of Aberfoil*
Drawn: J.C. Bentley (1809-1851) Engraved: J. Reddaway
*The Fray at Jean MacAlpine's Inn*
Drawn: G. Cruikshank (1792-1878) Engraved: S. Fisher
*Escape of Rob Roy at the Ford*
Drawn: S. Bough (1822-78) Engraved: W. Forrest
*Loch Ard*
Drawn: G.F. Robson Engraved: E.F. Finden (1791-1857)
Two in *ROB ROY:* Border Edition  1892-94
*Escape of Rob Roy*
Drawn: Sam Bough (1822-78) Engraved: Ch. de Billy
*Helen MacGregor*
Drawn and Engraved: R.W. MacBeth
Three in ROB ROY: Dryburgh Edition  1897
*Fight in the Inn at the Clachan of Aberfoil*
*The Murder of Morris*
*Rob Roy welcomed by his Clan*
Drawn: Lockhart Bogle Engraved: J.D. Cooper
*Flora MacIvor at the Waterfall* [Waverley: Border Edition]  1892-94
Drawn and Engraved: R.W. MacBeth
*Flora MacIvor at the Waterfall* [Waverley: A&C Black]  ND
Drawn: F.P. Stephanoff Engraved: R. Graves
Five in Skene's Sketches of Scenes from the Waverley Novels  1829
Drawn: James Skene (1775-1864) Engraver: Not Stated.
*Fort of Inversnaid; Lediart* (Ledard); *Ford of Alianan; Lochard; Clachan of Aberfoil*

**2. Illustrations of Scott's Poetical Works**
Wm. Miller engraved Turner's illustrations of Loch Katrine and Loch Achray to illustrate *The Lady of the Lake* for Lockhart's edition of *Scott's Poetical Works* (1834). *Loch Katrine* constituted the frontispiece, and *Loch Achray*, the vignette. (See Gerald Finley *Landscapes of Memory*.)
Drawn: J.M.W. Turner (1775-1851) Engraved: W. Miller (1796-1882)
The Royal Association for the Promotion of Fine Arts in Scotland published six engravings after Herdman illustrating *The Lady of the Lake* in 1868.
Drawn: Robert Herdman (1829-1888) Engraver: Not Stated
The Brig o' Bracklinn  1838
Drawn: J. Bentley Engraved: W.B. Cooke (1778-1853)

**3. Illustrated Books**
*Journey through Parts of North Britain*  1802
 8. *Ben Ledi* [F. Jukes (1748-1812)]
 9. *Loch-vana-choir* [F. Jukes]
 10. *Loch Achray* [S. Alken (1750-1815)]

11. *Cori-nan-Urishin* [S. Alken]
12. *Loch Kaitrin*, East-end [T. Medland (1755-1822)]
13. *Loch Kaitrin*, West-end [J. Walker]
14. *Hill of Binion* from the Lake [W. Pickett]
Drawn: Alexander Campbell Engraved: Various Engravers

*Scotia Depicta* 1803
*Kilmahog at the Entrance to the Pass of Leny* [The Trosacks]
Drawn: Jean Claude Nattes (1799) Engraved: James Fittler

*The Scenery of the Grampian Mountains* 1814
2. *Ben Lomond*, from the road on the north side of Loch Ard
7. *Ben Lomond*, from an elevated station on the braes of Strath Gartney, near the Trossachs
8. *Ben Venue*, from an eminence at the east end of Loch Achray
9. *Ben Venue and the Trossachs*, from the upper end of Loch Achray
10. *Ben Venue*, part of the east end of Loch Katrine, the Island, etc; from the road near Drum Baich Rock
11. *The West End of Loch Katerine*, Ben Venue in the distance, from the south shore
12. *Ben Ledi*, from the north side of the River Teith, above Callander
13. *Glen Finglass*, from a hill at its upper or western extremity: Ben Ledi in the distance.
Drawn: George Fennel Robson (1788-1833) Engraved: Henry Morton

*Scottish Tourist* Various Dates [1825]
*The Clachan and Vale of Aberfoyle*
*Loch Ard*
*Loch Katrine* [Perth AGM]
*Loch Achray* [Perth AGM]
Drawn and Engraved: W. Banks

*Vues Pittoresques d'Ecosse* 1827
*Falls of Inversnaid* [Edinburgh Libraries]
*Loch Katrine* [Perth AGM]
*Falls of Bracklinn* [Perth AGM]
Drawn: F.A. Pernot (1793-1865) Engraved: P. Lauters

*Lakes of Scotland* John Leighton 1834
*Loch Ard*
*Loch of Menteith*
*Loch Katrine and Helen's Isle, Looking South*
Drawn: J. Fleming (1792-1845) Engraved: Joseph Swan

*Scotland Illustrated* Wm. Beattie 1835
*Loch Katrine*
Drawn: Thos. Allom (1804-72) Engraved: R. Sands
*Loch Achray*
Drawn: Thos. Allom (1804-72) Engraved: J.C. Armitage (1820-97)
*Brackland Bridge*
Drawn: Thos. Allom (1804-72) Engraved: J.C. Varrall

*Perthshire Illustrated* 1843
*Lake of Monteith*
Drawn: A. Donaldson (1790-1846) Engraved: Wm. Bell Scott (1811-90)

*Scotland Delineated* John Parker Lawson 1847-54
73. *Loch Katrine* [Perth AGM: Lithograph]
Drawn: H. MacCulloch (1805-67) Engraved: E. Ciceri

74. *Loch Achray* [Lithograph]
Drawn: G.F. Robson Engraved: J. Graf
Black's *Picturesque Tourist of Scotland* 1851
*Loch Katrine*
Drawn: D. MacKenzie Engraved: Wm. Miller (1796-1882)
*Falls of Bracklinn* [Vignette]
Drawn: M. Stanley (1809-1844) Engraved: A. Branston
*The Charm of Old Scotland* Samuel G. Green 1886
*Ben Venue*
Drawn: T.L. Rowbotham Engraved: Ed. Whymper (1840-1911)
*Souvenir of Scotland* Thos. Nelson 1889
*Waterfall at Inversnaid, Loch Lomond*
*The Boathouse, Loch Katrine*
*Path by the Lake – Loch Katrine*
*Ben A'an from the Slope of Ben Venue*
*Ben Venue & Ellen's Isle – Loch Katrine*
*The Brig o' Turk*          [Chromolithographs]

**4. Miscellaneous Prints**
*Loch Katrine* [Nat Gall Scot] [Views] 1781
Drawn: Paul Sandby (1725-1809)

*Ellen's Isle, Loch Katrine* [Perth AGM] ND
Drawn: Unknown Engraved: Unknown

*View near the Trossachs* [Steel Engraving] c1821
Drawn: A. Nasmyth (1758-1840) Engraved: W. Richardson.

*Loch Ard, Perthshire* [Steel Engraving] c1821
Drawn: A. Nasmyth (1758-1840) Engraved: W. Richardson.

*Inversnaid Fort* [Vignette] c1821
Drawn: A. Nasmyth (1758-1840) Engraved: W.H. Lizars

*Pass of the Trosachs, Loch Katrine* [Vignette] c1840
Drawn: Thos. Allom (1804-72) Engraved: Robt. Wallis

*Falls of Inversnaid* [Colour Print] 1882
Artist: A.F. Lydon

* *Author's Collection*

## Appendix C

### Artists Associated With The Trossachs: A Summary List

**Joseph D. Adam** RSA 1842-96

Adam was a Glasgow landscape painter who later established an Art Studio at Craigmill near Stirling frequented by some of the Glasgow Boys, and other artists. He was a specialist in Highland Cattle.

| | | |
|---|---|---|
| 1887 | [Kelvingrove AGM] | December near Callander |
| 1891 | | Fording a Highland River: Glen Finlas |
| 1894 | | Summer: Loch Ard |
| 1896 | | Sunset after Storm: Loch Vennachar |

**Sam Bough** RSA 1822-78

A Cumbrian who was a pupil of Thomas Allom and became one of Scotland's leading landscape artists. He was Edinburgh based, but he used settings throughout Scotland, including the Trossachs.

| | | |
|---|---|---|
| 1865 | | Loch Achray |
| 1865 | | In the Trossachs |
| 1866 | | Vale of Teith |
| 1867 | | Ben Ledi from the Pass of Leny[w] |
| | | The Vale of the Teith from Lanerick |
| 1869 | | Ruins on Inch Mahon, Isle of Menteith |
| 1879 | | The River Teith at Callander, with |
| | [Hunterian AGM] | Ben Ledi in the distance |

**(Sir) David Young Cameron** RSA 1865-1945

Cameron was a contemporary of the Glasgow Boys, a much loved oil painter whose landscapes, particularly of mountain scenes, were very popular. He lived at Kippen from which there is a very striking view of the peaks of the Southern Highlands. He was most noted for his etchings.

| | | |
|---|---|---|
| 1903 | | Menteith |
| | [Smith AGM] | Ben Venue |
| | [Tate Gallery] | Ben Ledi, Early Spring |
| 1930 | | Loch Katrine |
| | | Menteith, Sundown |
| | [Hunterian] | (?) Loch Achray |

**Duncan Cameron** 1837-1916

Cameron was a Perthshire landscape painter who lived, at one time, in Stirling and was active in the Trossachs at the same time as the Glasgow Boys.

| | | |
|---|---|---|
| 1876 | | Cornfield at Brig o' Turk |
| 1880 | [Dundee AGM] | Loch Achray and Ben Venue |
| 1882 | | A November Day, Brig o' Turk |
| 1883 | | Ben Venue |
| | | *Crags, knolls confusedly hurled* |
| | | *The fragments of another world* |
| 1887 | | A Sunny Afternoon, Glenfinlas |

**James Docharty** ARSA 1829-78

Landscape painter from Bonhill in Dunbartonshire, influenced by James Milne Donald.

| | | |
|---|---|---|
| 1865 | | A Recollection of Loch Achray |
| 1867 | | The Silver Strand, Loch Katrine |
| | | Effect of Twilight, Loch Achray |
| 1868 | [Kelvingrove AGM] | Heart of the Trossachs |
| | | Head of Loch Vennachar |

1876                              Ben Venue and Loch Katrine
        [Kelvingrove AGM]        In the Trossachs
        [Dundee AGM]             The River Achray
1878                             The Trossachs

**David Farquharson** ARA ARSA 1839-1907
Landscape painter who was born in Blairgowrie and died in Birnam but was based in
England for much of his working life. His work achieved good atmospheric effects, was
well-liked
1885    [Kelvingrove AGM]        On the Achray
        [Dundee AGM]             On the Achray

**Alexander Fraser** RSA 1827-1899
A prolific landscape painter, friendly with Sam Bough and influenced by McCulloch. He
was an early enthusiast for plein air painting.
1871                             Ben Venue from the Silver Strand
1879                             The Old Pirn-mill on the Finglas
                                 Sunshine and Shower on Sron Armailte
        [Kelvingrove AGM]        Springtime, Dundarroch, Brig o'Turk
1880                             Loch Achray
                                 Ben-y-Glas Ferry: Midsummer
1883                             In the Heart of the Trossachs

**Everett Galloway** fl 1918-1962
Twentieth century landscape painter who worked in Perthshire, and in Northern Ireland.
He lived at one time at Inverteith, Callander.
1918-40  [Perth AGM]            Loch Vennacher and Ben Venue from
                                 Invertrossachs(w)

**(Sir) James Guthrie** PRSA 1859-1930
One of the more famous of the Glasgow Boys, he went, with Walton, to Brig o' Turk in
1779 where they were joined by Crawhall.
1881                             The Cottar's Garden
1881                             Paid Off
1881                             Gypsy Fire's are Burning for Daylight's
                                 Past and Gone
1881-2   [Kelvingrove AGM]       A Funeral Service in the Highlands

**George Henry** 1858-1943
One of the Glasgow Boys, a pupil of W.Y. MacGregor, who joined Guthrie and Crawhall
at Brig o' Turk in 1879-81.
        c1881                    The Cottage on the Hill
        1882    [Kelvingrove AGM]   Brig o' Turk

**George Whitton Johnstone** 1849-1901
Born in Glamis, Johnstone painted in a 'Dutch' style.
1895                             On the Finglas Water
                                 An Autumn Day in the Trossachs
1896                             A Mountain Stream in the Trossachs
1900                             In the Trossachs
                                 A Peep at Loch Vennachar
        [Smith AGM]             Lake of Menteith

**Archibald Kay** ARSA 1860-1935
Kay, who was President of the Glasgow Art Club, lived at Woodend, Kilmahog. He was
a well-liked landscape painter active in his own locality, pre-eminently upon the Leny.
1904                             Spate in the Highlands

| 1908 | [Smith AGM] | Ben Ledi |
| 1912 | | Loch Vennachar and Ben Venue |
| 1914 | | Autumn at Kilmahog, Callander |
| 1914 | | Storm in the Pass of Leny |
| 1915 | | On the Road to Loch Katrine |
| 1915 | | Black Donald's Lynn, Pass of Leny |
| 1923 | | Ben Venue and Loch Achray |
| 1932 | | The New Road to the Trossachs |
| 1933 | | Springtime in the Trossachs |
| ND | [Smith AGM] | O' river of winter sunshine |

**Joseph Bartholemew Kidd** RSA 1808-1889

Kidd was a pupil of Thomson of Duddingston, several of whose Highland landscapes seem to have been produced in the Trossachs:

| 1830 | Loch Achray by Moonlight |
| 1832 | Ben Venue from Loch Achray |
| 1836 | The Trossachs, from the Inn |
| | Loch Achray with the Trossachs |

**(Sir) John Lavery** RSA 1856-1941

Lavery was perhaps the best known of the Glasgow Boys, but not particularly associated with the Trossachs, except that his portraits of Graham took him to Gartmore.

| 1895 | [Kelvingrove AGM] | R.B. Cunninghame Graham |
| | | Mrs Cunninghame Graham |
| | [National Gallery] | Loch Katrine |

**William Leighton Leitch** 1804-1883

Painter of atmospheric watercolours, pupil of Knox, and contemporary with and influenced by McCulloch and Bough. He had the distinction of teaching Queen Victoria how to paint.

| 1870 | Ben Venue from Loch Achray |
| 1875 | Hillside Balquither, Perthshire |
| 1878 | Ben Venue from the Trossachs |

**Horatio McCulloch** RSA 1805-1867

McCulloch's views of Loch Katrine and of Glencoe provide the quintessential mid-Victorian image of Scottish scenery, in the same way as Landseer's *Stag at Bay* epitomised wild sports of the Highlands. He was Knox's pupil and influenced many, many others.

| 1837 | | View near Aberfoyle |
| 1843 | | Loch Katrine from the Boathouse |
| 1844 | | Loch Ard: Sunset |
| 1845 | | On the Avendhu: Ben Lomond in the Distance |
| 1847 | | Inversnaid Ferry, Loch Lomond |
| 1860 | | Loch Achray and the Trossachs |
| 1862 | | Ben Venue: Loch Katrine from near the Silver Strand |
| 1864 | [Kelvingrove AGM] | Loch Achray: Evening |
| | | or 'Sundown: Loch Achray' |
| | | Mill in Glenfinlas |
| 1865 | [Kelvingrove AGM] | Loch Achray: Morning |
| 1866 | [Perth AGM] | Loch Katrine |

**McNeil Macleay** c1802-1878

Macleay lived in Stirling, a portrait painter who turned to landscape with the advent of photography.

| 1862 | At the Mill of Cardross, Vale of Menteith |
| 1869 | On the Loch of Menteith: Ben Lomond in the Distance |
| 1870 | On Loch Ard: Ben Lomond in the Distance |

**John MacWhirter** RA 1839-1911
MacWhirter was a famous Scottish landscape painter whom Ruskin promoted, and who often visited Adam's Craigmill studio. His highly competent, colourful pictures made him much admired. He was an early postcard artist.

| 1867 | Inchmahome; Autumn Evening |

**Arthur Melville** 1855-1904
The leading 'Scottish Impressionist' Melville followed Guthrie, Henry and Walton in going to Brig o' Turk.

| 1884 | Loch Vennacher |
| | The Shieling, Brig o' Turk |

**Sir John Everett Millais** 1829-96
In addition to this paintings Millais filled two sketch books containing highly finished drawings and sketches when he was in Glenfinlas with Ruskin.

| 1853 | Effie [Gray] |
| 1854 | John Ruskin |
| 1854 | Landscape Study of Waterfall |

**Alexander B Monro** 1805-1891
Monro lived at Auchenbowie House, Stirling, and was a painter of landscapes and seascapes.

| 1843 | Cottages at Brig o' Turk, Glenfinlas |
| 1868 | View near Callander: Loch Vennachar |
| | Loch of Menteith: Moonlight |

**Alexander Nasmyth** 1758-1840
Nasmyth was a prolific and influential landscape painter who based his early work on the great eighteenth century continental painters. Loch Katrine was a favourite subject of his. His A 'Highland Landscape with Ruined Temple' is probably Loch Katrine and is like a Claude; no such temple exists, of course:

| 1810 | Bridge of Bracklynn (w) |
| 1812 | The River and Wooden Bridge at Loch Katrine |
| 1813 | Pass of the Cows, Loch Katrine |
| 1814 | Entrance to Loch Katrine |
| 1836 | The Brig of Turk (w) |
| 1835 | Ben Venue and Loch Achray |
| | Ben Lomond from Loch Ard |

**Waller Hugh Paton** RSA 1828-1895
Born in Dunfermline, Paton was a pupil of John Adam Houston whose landscapes were often characterised by a more intimate approach than those of his contemporaries. He is said to have been the first Scottish painter to finish landscapes on the spot. His nephew Ranald Noel Paton (1864-1943) lived in Menteith at the end of his life.

| 1854 | Loch Achray |
| 1855 | Loch Vennachar |
| 1859 | Outlet of Loch Achray |
| | The Ash Trees, Loch Achray |
| | Loch Achray |
| 1871 | Ben Venue from Duncraggan |

**Arthur Perigal** 1816-1884
A talented Edinburgh painter influenced by McCulloch, and later one of his rivals,who, between 1837 and 1844, produced a number of local landscapes which were very successful.

| | |
|---|---|
| 1837 | On the Teith near Callander |
| 1838 | View of Ben Ledi from Kilmahog |
| | Scene near the Brig of Turk with Ben Venue |
| | The Trossachs |
| 1844 | Benan: Scene among the Trossachs |
| | Falls of the Achray, Trossachs |

**John Smart** RSA 1838-1899
John Smart was a regular visitor to Adam's Craigmill studio. His pictures demonstrated his 'ardent passion for his native land' (Irwin). Rev William Wilson said his best picture was 'The Heat of the Day', of Loch Achray.

| | | |
|---|---|---|
| 1838 | | View near Kinlochard |
| | | Moor near Port of Menteith: Rain Coming On |
| | | Rain Clouds crossing the Valley near Aberfoyle |
| 1871 | | Loch Achray, Trossachs and Ben Venue |
| 1886 | [Dundee AGM] | The Pass of Leny, Perthshire |
| 1886 | | In the Land of the MacGregor |
| 1894 | | In Fair Menteith |
| 1894 | [Smith AGM] | A Perthshire River |

**James Stevenson** d1844
An Edinburgh landscape painter who was one of the first to produce a number of canvases in the district following the popularity brought to it by Scott.

| | |
|---|---|
| 1809 | On the Road, Callander to Trossachs |
| 1810 | View of Lochend |
| | Loch Achray, Perthshire |
| 1812 | View between Doune and Callander |
| | Loch Ard |
| 1827 | The Head of Loch Katrine |
| 1828 | Waterfall near Loch Katrine |
| | Loch Achray, near Loch Katrine |

**John Thomson** (of Duddingston) 1778-1840
Thomson followed his friend, Sir Walter Scott, to the Trossachs. Like Scott's his work was very significant in attracting visitors to the Highlands.

| | |
|---|---|
| 1824 | Coir-nan-Uruiskin |
| 1827 | Loch Katrine from Coir-nan-Uruiskin |
| 1828 | Glen near Loch Ketrin |

**Joseph William Mallord Turner** 1775-1851
Turner remains Britain's greatest landscape painter. He may have been in the Trossachs at the turn of the century, and he definitely visited the district in 1831 in order to prepare illustrations for an edition of Scott's Poetical Works.

| | | |
|---|---|---|
| 1800 | [Fitzwilliam Museum] | Mountain Landscape with Lake |
| | | or 'In the Trossachs' |
| 1832 | | Loch Katrine |
| 1832 | | Loch Achray |

**Edward Arthur Walton** 1860-1922
One of the Glasgow Boys, was at Brig o' Turk in 1879 and 1881, painting 'rural' subjects.

| | | |
|---|---|---|
| 1879 | [Dundee AGM] | The Brig o' Turk |
| 1881 | | The Wayfarer |

BOOK REVIEWS

**Mining: from Kirkintilloch to Clackmannan and Stirling to Slammanan.** Guthrie Hutton. Stenlake, £12.95.

Last of a five book history of Scottish mining, this is profusely illustrated, with some emphasis on Clackmannanshire which through the 17th and 18th centuries was the biggest coal exporting area in the country. It had daily trainloads to Alloa harbour pre1900. The 'thousands of tons a day for 50 years' forecast for the post WWII Glenochills failed NCB drift mine is noted, also the 'walk in' Tillicoultry mine of the 1870s and its reconstruction post WWII with the first underground television broadcasts. This is a welcome resource for Forth area history.

**Reminiscences of Dollar and Tillicoultry – and other districts adjoining the Ochils.** William Gibson. 1882. Latest reprint. Strong Oak Press. 240pp. 1 871048 23 0. £12.95.

A local history 'classic'.

**Clackmannan and the Ochils: an illustrated architectural guide.** Adam Swan. Rutland Press. 152pp. 1 873 190 530. £10.95.

This new edition launched with an exhibition at RIAS in June and in August at Alloa Tower, is produced with some striking photography, including colour. The 1987 edition was drawing attention to a much neglected area, now this 'wee county' is seeing a regeneration with admirable initiatives by the Tower/Heritage Trust, the Council, Ochil View Housing and others, and coping with industrial and other changing events. The revision has been thorough and pleasing making the book a must guide to the area, an information source and interest pleasure to visitors and locals, akin to over 20 similar architectural guides in this RIAS/Rutland series, including *Stirling and the Trossachs.*

Of particular local interest this book describes the award winning restoration of Alloa Tower, though in doing so it sadly neglects to acknowledge the influence of many years insistance and activities of the Clackmannanshire Field Studies Society (CFSS), many of whose members constitute the ongoing Friends of Alloa Tower. Especially no memtion is made of the 1972 and subsequent editions of the CFSS's basic book *Alloa Tower and the Erskines of Mar* – whose 1987 edition, and partial opening event, really emphasised the critical need for restoration of the crunbling fabric, as did the thesis of the CFSS chairman's daughter Elizabeth Roxburgh, whose supervisor Bob Heath became its architect. The Tower and this book are significant in this ongoing regeneration of a once neglected area.

**World Tartans**. Iain Zaczek. Collins and Brown. 480pp. Hbk £12.99.

Richly illustrated, short descriptions, brief history and changes, are given for 250 Scottish and 200 others.

Some of passing interest to the Forth area were noticed – Bruce, Campbell, Drummond – with links to Drymen / Lennox / Prince Charlie, Erskine, Falkirk, Ferguson, Graham, Lennox, Stirling and Bannockburn – introduced by Wilson of Bannockburn c1847, Braveheart Warrior – three by the makers of the film and by King a hire company, Caledonian Society – with links to Macpherson and Duff of Braco, Rob Roy – a specimen was collected by the Highland Society of London c1815, Scottish Knights Templar, Scottish Parliament, Sir Walter Scott, Tartan Army.

**Editorial Notes**

*Sir William Wallace*

An interesting postscript to the Wallace related papers in FNH volumes 21 and 22 (1998 and 1999) is an extract from the Wallace Society Newsletter (October) –

" ... two Regency tables carved from the wood of the famous Wallace Oak in Elderslie, that fell in a storm in the mid 1800s, sold at auction for over £80,000! The buyer was reported to be a film buff from London. As the Wallace connection with the tree is only legend, it shows the power that Wallace's memory still commands...."

*Forthcoming*

Th Annual Symposium and Journal

The FNH Board intends to continue the annual *Man and the Landscape* symposia – presently on the 27th – and occasion them each November to launch the annual *Forth Naturalist and Historian* journal – presently on volume 24. The next issue of FNH (volume 25, November 2002) will include – papers/ proceedings from the History Department's March 2002 conference *The Thistle and the Rose 1502-13*, to complement and coincide with a major exhibition in Stirling Castle to commemorate the 500th anniversary of the 1502 Treaty of Perpetual Peace! – till the battle of Flodden 1513!

**Author Addresses**

Corbett, L., Hon Sec FNH, Biological Sciences, University of Stirling, FK9 4LA.
Cowley, David, RCAHMS, 16 Bernard Terrace, Edinburgh, EH8 9NX.
Harrison, S.J., Environmental Science, University of Stirling, FK9 4LA.
Henty, C.J., Psychology, University of Stirling, FK9 4LA.
Inglis, Bill, 6 Dargai Terrace, Dunblane, FK16 6AV.
Joynson, Peter, Laraich, Aberfoyle, FK8 3TQ.
Mackay, K.J.H., Hayford House, Cambusbarron, FK7 9PR.
Perkins, Chris, Hermitage Woodland, Old Parsonage, Croachy, Strathnairn, IV2 6JE.
Spooner, David, 96 Halbeath Road, Dunfermline, KY12 7LR.
Stewart, J.A., 109 Greenbank Crescent, Edinburgh, EH10 5TA.
Stott, Louis, 10 Trossachs Road, Aberfoyle, FK8 3SW.
Tipping, Richard, Environmental Science, University of Stirling, FK9 4LA.
Waldron, Richard, Environmental Science, University of Stirling, FK9 4LA.

## THE FORTH NATURALIST AND HISTORIAN

The Forth Naturalist and Historian (FNH) is an informal enterprise of Stirling University. It was set up in 1975 by several University and Central Regional Council staff to provide a focus for interests, activities and publications of environmental, heritage and historical studies for the Forth area, comprising now local authority areas Stirling, Falkirk and Clackmannanshire.

The promotion of an annual environment/heritage symposium called *Man and the Landscape* has been a main feature, and this year, the 27th, it's on Loch Lomond and the Trossachs – Scotland's first National Park.

The annual *Forth Naturalist and Historian* has since 1975 published numerous papers, many being authoritative and significant in their field, and includes annual reports of the weather, and of birds in the locality, plus book reviews and notes. These volumes (24 as of 2001) provide a valuable successor to that basic resource *The Transactions of the Stirling Field and Archaeological Society*, 1878-1939. Five year contents/indexes are available, and selected papers are published in pamphlet form, while others eg. Ashfield Factory Village, The Weather and Bird Reports, and Flora papers, can be available as reprints.

A major publication is the 230 page *Central Scotland – Land, Wildlife, People* 1994, a natural history and heritage survey, and used in schools throughout the area, also in the form of a CD-Rom, *Heart of Scotland's Environment* (HSE).

Other FNH and associated publications still in print include – *Mines and Minerals of the Ochils, Airthrey and Bridge of Allan, The Making of Modern Stirling, Woollen Mills of the Hillfoots, The Ochil Hills* – landscape, wildlife, heritage – an introduction with walks, *Alloa Tower and the Erskines of Mar*, and the *Lure of Loch Lomond* a journey round the shores and islands. Several of these are in association with Clackmannanshire Field Studies Society. Godfrey Maps have collaborated in producing old Ordnance Survey large scale maps of the 1890s for some 20 places in the area.

FNH publications are listed on the internet by Book Data (thebookplace.com), British Library (BLPC) and by booksellers eg Amazon, Bol, Barnes and Noble....

Offers of papers/notes for publication, and of presentations for symposia are ever welcome.

Honorary Secretary Lindsay Corbett,
University of Stirling, FK9 4LA, and 30 Dunmar Drive, Alloa.
Tel: 01259 215091. Fax: 01786 494994.
E-mail: lindsay.corbett@stir.ac.uk
Web: http://www.stir.ac.uk/departments/naturalsciences/Forth_naturalist